HOW DID WE GET TO BE SO DIFFERENT?

SS O'CONNOR

First published in Great Britain by Otium Press 2023

www.otiumpress.com

A CIP catalogue record for this book is available from the British Library

ISBN 978-1-7391559-1-9

Cover and end papers: Details from Pink Cava Lily by Bruce McLean.
Copyright, the artist. Published by CCA Galleries, London and printed by Coriander Studios.
Reproduced by kind permission of Bruce McLean and the CCA Galleries, September, 2022

Book design and art direction: Ash Gibson
Photo editor: Cat Costelloe

Type set in Adobe Garamond, Brandon Grotesque and NY Irvin.

Printed and bound in the UK by The Pureprint Group

OTIUM PRESS

Grand Union Studios, 332 Ladbroke Grove, London, W10 5AD
info @otiumpress.com

For Gillie

The Secrets of Life Quartet

The Secrets of Life:
From Big Bang to Trump

BOOK ONE

HOW DID LIFE END UP WITH US?

SS O'CONNOR

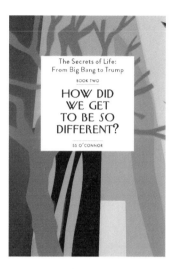

The Secrets of Life:
From Big Bang to Trump

BOOK TWO

HOW DID WE GET TO BE SO DIFFERENT?

SS O'CONNOR

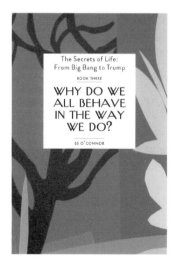

The Secrets of Life:
From Big Bang to Trump

BOOK THREE

WHY DO WE ALL BEHAVE IN THE WAY WE DO?

SS O'CONNOR

The Secrets of Life:
From Big Bang to Trump

BOOK FOUR

SO WHAT DOES IT ALL MEAN?

SS O'CONNOR

The Secrets of Life:
From Big Bang to Trump

BOOK TWO

HOW DID WE GET TO BE SO DIFFERENT?

SS O'CONNOR

OTIUM PRESS

Before and after. But how did we change so
much in just a blink of evolutionary time?

INTRODUCTION

As I came to the end of the first volume of what was to become this quartet of books, I found myself more and more baffled that mankind should ever have emerged at all. How unlikely it now seemed to me that life could have somehow started on earth around 3.8 billion years ago, and yet for all that time it had conformed to the same forces of competition and cooperation that had eventually created the biosphere.

And then we came along - and in an incredibly short span of time we managed to arrive at an entirely new take it all.

Of course the evolutionary process had already thrown up some extraordinarily bizarre varieties and adaptations before us: things that existed in wafer-thin ecological niches with astoundingly inventive behavioural strategies. Nonetheless, it still seemed amazing that a species like us could have arisen from the same maelstrom that created these, and yet we would do things that none of them had ever attempted before.

How, in particular, could we speak, reason, argue, develop our imaginations, dream up the mysteries and fantasies we wrap ourselves in, die for passionate causes, laugh and love, take each other so seriously and yet be capable of such vileness, be self-healing yet self-condemning, so purposefully destructive but also so caring? Nothing else could combine these things; nothing else came close.

And, above all, how would our species develop the ability to look forward, to imagine the future and to make its own decisions about how to react and behave? Instead of being shaped and controlled by the force of an evolutionary software that dictated our outcomes, why would we alone decide on so much for ourselves?

One of the major differences between us and everything that had developed before, was that we were determined to be in charge of our lives - and not to follow the dictates of our genes. Before we came along, everything had stuck to the rules, evolving over vast timescales of achingly slow progress, and coming up with minute changes, largely as the result of blind mutations. Yet we were now going to turn all this on its head.

How odd it seemed to me that after 99.995% of the time there'd been life on earth, we would introduce entirely new ways of doing things. The planet was by now largely settled in its structure and practices, yet we were going to barge into the biosphere and dominate life as nothing had ever done before. And we were only to take a few millennia to do it - blinks in evolutionary time - instead of the millions of years that other organisms had needed.

How did all this happen? And why did the changes we came up with make us hurtle along at such a bewildering pace?

One of the most remarkable things about our story was that we'd had such an inauspicious start. We began as a feeble creature with few natural assets, living up trees, and propelled by a very ordinary intelligence. Yet we were made of the same cellular stuff as everything else, we'd arisen from the same evolutionary processes, been subject to the same genetic drives, and shaped by the same programming to survive and prosper. But we were destined to be the first organisms to deliberately move away from their animal origins. How did we achieve things that nothing else had ever come close to, in spite of them being around for far longer than us? What were the steps that took us so far… and further and further away from our origins?

Unlike other life forms we were going to accept leaders who demanded tight control over our communities, even though they would bully and suppress us. They'd also frequently assume too many rewards for doing it. Yet we'd tolerate them, even idolise them. Why was that, when we should have been telling them to pipe down? And why, amongst other things, were we so keen to live in hierarchies and to accept the destructive pecking orders that this involved, even though we'd come to realise how unfair they could be?

Over time we learnt to survive by imitating others, and accepting the memes we'd inherited about how to live - but why would we go along with this approach when so many people around us were plainly getting things wrong?

If we were descended from billions of years of trial, error, success and inheritance, then surely we'd be like everything else in being genetically determined? Yet while we've self-evidently shrugged off chunks of this heritage, just how much of us is down to our ancestry, and how much is due to our own decisions? Are we really responsible for our thoughts and feelings, our actions and choices, or did these come from others, or even from inner drives that we're only vaguely aware of?

Why did we take such gigantic leaps as we evolved, and how could these changes come about in such an absurdly short time? Why did we create our own rules for living, and how would we manage our societies while quelling our interior lives? What were the reasons for us putting up with obvious winners and losers in life, when we were all in it together? Successful symbioses abounded in the natural world, but why were we humans prepared to accept such small proportions of the benefits when we entered into our own versions of them?

And possibly most baffling of all the questions one might ask about us was how we were going to balance the drives of our competitive inheritance against our recognition that cooperation could get us to where we wanted to go? The forces of collaboration and conflict were coming down on us as they did on everything else - but how were we going to respond to the collision of interests they so plainly represented?

And where was this going to end up?

SS O'Connor
Somerset, June 2022

The Big Man... you're going to be hearing
a lot more from him - for a very long time.

CHAPTER ONE

AFTER 3.8 BILLION YEARS OF LIFE ON EARTH WE'VE FINALLY GOT TO AN INTERESTING BIT, A SPECIES THAT WE CAN ALL UNDERSTAND... US! BUT IF HUMANS ARE SO SPECIAL, WHERE DID WE COME FROM? AND WHY HAVE WE CHANGED SO UTTERLY IN SUCH A SHORT PERIOD? ANTHROPOLOGISTS AND EVOLUTIONARY BIOLOGISTS TALK ABOUT THE REVOLUTIONS THAT MADE US. BUT WHAT ARE THEY?

As the Guru said, you wouldn't expect to understand an ocean by looking at the waves. Nor would you expect to appreciate the secrets of the natural world just by examining the things we can see - the phenotypes of the different life forms. In much the same way, many of us can become frustrated when we try to understand ourselves by looking into our psychology, or philosophies, cultures, social contracts, knowledge, the role of the spirit, language, logic…all these and many more.

But important though these things are, they can never tell the full story because if these are the ingredients that add up to make the pie that life has cooked… then what was the recipe? Don't we have to look at the underlying forces that led to humans producing these effects in the first place?

'Human evolution, at first, seems extraordinary. How could the process that gave rise to slugs and oak trees and fish produce a creature that can fly to the moon and invent the internet and cross the ocean in boats?'
Stephen Pinker, *The Blank Slate*

Perhaps we have to start with our origins? And that's not easy because the debates that go on among biologists and anthropologists about when and where we began, and what the early stages of our development were, just seem to get ever more complicated as time passes. Even the name for the people we've evolved into is a bit of a mystery. We call ourselves *Homo sapiens* - wise - but nobody ever seems to completely agree on what's so clever about us. If we're reckoned to be wise, then what were our forebears like - and why weren't they as intelligent as us?

One of the problems, of course, is that the evidence that's needed to make a clear narrative about our past is so fragmentary and elusive. New digs, and things like the contents of recently discovered caves, have a habit of producing ever more tiny shards of bone remains. But when these are examined and pored over by the latest kit, have their genomes sequenced and so on, they often suggest that there's yet another chapter to be written about the evolutionary branching that came before us.

However, if one held a gun to most anthropologists' heads and told them they had to summarise the scientific opinions about which twig on the taxonomic tree had ended up with humans, and when we all originally arrived, they'd probably nod to the view that there were three major stages of development that we went through before modern humans came along around 200,000 years ago.

First, there were a number of ape-like ancestors that were pretty successful for about three million years before they became extinct. Then there were the early *Homo* species that took things on for another couple of million years until these, too, died out - but not before a branch had evolved into what biologists label 'later *Homo*'. These were among the numerous sub-species that were by then living in different parts of the world - and it's from some of these that we ended up with us lot - what some people refer to as *sapiens*.

> '*Homo sapiens* is a tiny twig on an improbable
> branch of a contingent limb on a fortunate tree.'
> Stephen Jay Gould, *The Richness of Life*

As a species we started in small numbers, and until fairly recently, we've stayed small. It's really only in the last two or three hundred years, during which we've got on top of a whole range of life-threatening issues like disease and violence, that our population has shot forward to where we are now. Amazingly, largely because of the ways we limited our clan sizes, if you were to add up every one of us that's ever lived, I reckon that something like seven per cent of the entire *H. sapiens* species - ever since it first began - is alive at the present day.

But what happened in the long past to make us who we are? What allowed us to turn from the relatively feeble, thin-skinned, blunt toothed and clawless things we used to be into the apex predators we've become? What were the underlying currents that developed our natures and our way of viewing each other and the world? These revolutions that people talk about - what were they and how did they change us from being forest-dwelling creatures into the Nobel prize winners and sexy film stars we are today?

Two of the revolutions occurred during the time of our ancient ancestors, creatures that lived before the *Homo* species even emerged, and of whom all trace has completely disappeared. But we've inherited their genes, and the way they evolved tells us much about ourselves. So what's their part in it all?

The story seems to begin about seven or eight million years ago when a forebear of ours was the origin of the split between the hominids - from which we're descended - and the chimps and bonobos that remain our closest living relatives. Further branching of the evolutionary tree led down to the various ape species, and the effect of this process has left us with the extraordinary fact that although we share something like 99% of our DNA with our chimpanzee cousins… we're genetically closer to them than they are to gorillas.

At some point in this splitting process we lost a pair of chromosomes. We have 46 and the great apes have 48. This alone has led some people to the conclusion that we're completely different to them, and therefore that we couldn't share a common ancestor. But the weight of scientific opinion these days is that some of them must have somehow fused together, yet the merged chromosome in us still manages to retain much of the genetic information there'd been there before.

We all started out in the Rift Valley of East Africa, now a glorious magnet for swanky safaris, but then a deeply wooded forest. What were we like? As far as anyone can deduce, there were a number of small groups of competing genera that would have had similar but differing characteristics. In general they were all small-brained, ape-like, hairy things that lived on fruit, roots and nuts and would almost certainly have spent a lot of their time up trees.

The colonies they formed would have been geographically very concentrated to begin with, and the dispersal of our various types of ancestor was limited for millions of years, although eventually they seemed to have gone west a bit over to Chad, and also southwards, down towards Tanzania and beyond.

Although there must have been variety between the various types, all these early species are thought to have looked much the same with their flat faces, high cheekbones and immensely powerful facial muscles and teeth that could grind their way through a diet of hard foods. Meat eating on any scale didn't seem to start for another three million or so years after we'd first turned up.

As to our origins up trees, even now this has left us with our strong grip, opposable thumbs, and a pretty good balance mechanism for such upright creatures. An intriguing echo of our forest years shows up if you put your finger under the toes of a newborn baby then watch them curl round as the tiny foot instinctively tries to hold on to its mother or an imaginary branch.

A number of early genera must have come and gone, but in the 1920s scientists identified one they named *Australopithecus*, or the 'Southern Ape'. From this they think three or four different species would have split off, and it's at this point that we begin to diverge markedly from our primate backgrounds.

Among the most significant of the fossil evidence from around this period are bones from a 3.2 million-year-old female that anthropologists have named Lucy. What's interesting about the bits they've identified from her skeleton is that they show a number of fractures that look as if they were the result of falling from a great height… no doubt out of a tree. Poor old Luce.

Now if you took a poll of the experts about when the first recognisable '*Homo*' branch originated you'd probably find that most would put it at around 2.8 million years ago. It was then that the three species that evolved around the Lake Rudolf area in northern Kenya first arose. *Homo rudolfensis* are the ones who are thought to have first used stone tools, *Homo habilis* (which means 'handy man', I kid you not, because they became very skilled at splitting and handling sharp rocks) and *Homo erectus*, who stood upright and was the one whose lines survived when it left Africa, and evolved towards the different species that lead down to modern man. (And who also, of course, provides the class clown with many a hilarious gag.)

However, it was almost certainly a hominid genus that lived before these ancestor species of ours came along who was responsible for the first of the revolutionary breakthroughs… *walking upright*. The prime suspect for this breakthrough is an ape-like creature called *Sahelanthropus tchadensis*, and the reason it's been credited with the novelty of getting up off four legs is because fragments of its skull have been found that show its neck was positioned directly below the head, as ours is, rather than being held horizontally, like the chimpanzees.

Why was walking such a big deal? After all, dinosaurs did it and their bird descendants inherited the trick. Some types of reptile even manage to get up off four legs and onto two when they want a burst of speed. But what made us so unusual was that we mastered what's known as the bipedal gait: where one foot is placed alternatively in front of another, rather than shuffling, or hopping around on both of them together. This bipedal process is unknown among amphibians and, actually, is now used by very few mammals other than primates.

Many of our distant ape relations, particularly gibbons and chimps, can also walk for short periods with limited support, frequently getting up on two legs as a way of increasing their feeding range. To do this they'll wrap their feet around a thin branch, and use their hands to grab supporting branches to get them further out into the forest canopy to where the sweeter and fresher leaves grow on the outer parts of trees.

Where early man completely departed from his ancestors, however, was in evolving profound changes to his anatomy. Over time the size of the pelvis reduced, and then changed shape in a way that gave greater leverage to the muscles that allowed the hips to swing. Our toes got shorter, the thigh bones moved round to point inwards and our spines curved into an 'S' shape to make the body's weight align over our hips. The cumulative effect of these changes was to put our feet under the centre of our bodies and to cushion the brain from being bashed up and down by the new walking motion.

Walk like an 'S'

But why did all this happen? As usual… blame the weather. Anthropologists think that what took man from feeding up trees to full-blooded walking was a long-term climate change crisis that, paradoxically, led to a species bloom that began about 2.6 million years ago. It was then that East Africa began to dry out and open savannahs eventually took the place of dense forests.

Over a relatively short period of time the ability to stand up and look farther out became a huge evolutionary advantage. Not only could we now spot what was available to eat… but it was also possible to see what was trying to eat us. It must have been around this time that mankind began to find dead game, and then use their new stone tool technology to unlock the highly nutritious bone marrow that other scavengers like vultures and jackals couldn't reach. In time, meat became a key part of these people's diet, and consuming it unlocked a higher energy source than the other kinds of food they were used to. And much of this energy went on increasing the size of the brain.

Being upright on two legs also freed the hands for carrying rudimentary weapons. These would have helped in defending early man from wild animals, and they'd also, no doubt, have been a handy addition for the endless skirmishing that preserved territorial rights against neighbouring tribes. It was around now that using stone tools and sharp sticks became an everyday extension to man's limited abilities.

Taken together, the use of tools were added to the advantages of being upright, and this unleashed another of those 1+1=3 leaps that so often lead to accelerated progress in the natural world.

Having one's arms and hands free also allowed early *Homo* species to carry food back to the rest of the colony. This must have greatly extended their feeding range and, doubtless, played its part in separating male tasks from the more stationary female demands of nursing small children.

Perhaps it even led to some kind of gender split as females began to make foraging and gathering their principal area of work, probably because they wouldn't then have had to move too far from their offspring? Is it too big an assumption to say that this might have been the period when the division of labour that's seen so frequently in the natural world could have taken root in our embryonic culture too?

'We owe the origin and development of human society and, consequently, of culture and civilisation, to the fact that work performed under the division of labour is more productive than when performed in isolation.'
Ludwig von Mises, *Human Action*

Adding these things together makes it clear how mankind's evolutionary breakthroughs shot forward once we'd started outsourcing our solutions. We now had weapons to lessen our vulnerability, sharp tools to scavenge game, and a way of moving around that hugely extended our horizons.

But walking was just the beginning. Because what happened next seems to have had an even greater influence on our cultural development. We began to *run*.

Like me, you'd probably think that running was just a simple extension of our success in walking, and that moving faster was a case of making one leg go in front of the other a little quicker. Anatomists tell us, however, that running involves completely different biomechanics, and much had to change for the body to create the 'mass spring' mechanism that was needed for us to end up with Usain Bolt. Without the tendons and ligaments being adapted to stretch and contract, the body would never have been able to release the kind of energy needed to get our rates up.

One of the problems that arises with running is that the body becomes far less stable the quicker it moves, and the whole interplay of connective tissue has to adapt and strengthen, particularly to support the cranium. Without some kind of elastic tethering mechanism, the head would wobble around alarmingly on top of a rushing body, something that would be made all the worse by moving over uneven ground.

The answer was to develop ligaments that could stabilise the skull, and meant growing a ridge on the inside of it to anchor them. Because of this, when anthropologists look at the skull finds of early man, they've concluded that the ability to get up on our sprinting toes didn't get underway until the *H. erectus* species arrived around two million years ago.

There were other changes needed as well if we were to increase our speeds. We had to grow longer legs relative to our body mass, develop larger joint surfaces to absorb the greater shock that came from increasing the body's momentum when landing, and evolve stronger spinal and gluteal muscles to stabilise the torso. Then we had to somehow come up with the plantar arch in our feet that could give our bodies the elastic springiness so necessary for loping along.

'Running didn't just make people… it also made them better people.'
Christopher McDougall, *Born to Run*

These adaptations must have taken thousands of years, but they marked the point at which humans were able to literally bound forward in our evolutionary development. However, there were major prizes to be won from doing it as the changes allowed us to see and arrive at dead game faster, and to scavenge it before other animals arrived.

Far more importantly, we found we could increase our chances of finding fresh meat by… killing it. We became *hunters*.

And what were the prey? Large, four legged animals in the main. But why them? You'd think that it would have been far easier to hunt smaller things because anything big would have had the acceleration and top speeds to see off a human? And, doubtless, a few ways of tearing us apart if we got too close.

That may be true, but quadrupeds all share a common weakness in that they have to coordinate the respiration rate with their running gait. Otherwise they'd knock the air out of their lungs. Now our human ancestors began to exploit their point of difference because, by being on two legs, they weren't having their chest cavities compressed when they landed, and were therefore able to vary their breathing to their stride length.

Another of our great advantages was that we could alter our diets to suit the conditions, and then to lope along for long periods on relatively little. The result of these factors was that early hunters were able to keep going for hours on end by varying their speeds and gaits.

This all led to us developing endurance running techniques that scientists believe aren't matched by any other species in the natural world, with the arguable exception of wolves at low speeds. The result was an athletic capacity that allowed early man to wear down larger and fiercer animals through a process that anthropologists have termed 'persistence hunting'.

The key to success with this strategy was to get after an animal when the sun's at its hottest, and then force it to keep running until overheating sets in and it's brought to exhaustion. These early hominids had to do this because they didn't have spears or bows and arrows, and they'd have had to get close enough to kill things by stabbing them with sharpened sticks.

It was probably also around this time that a useful mutation meant that man lost his body hair. Larger animals generally have a fur covering and this means they rely on panting air over their tongues to cool themselves down. Now without a shaggy pelt, our ancestors found they could dissipate heat by surface sweating, and this thermoregulatory advantage became yet another asset in outlasting their prey.

Some anthropologists have even added a twist to this by saying that because we were now upright, the only protection we needed was to the top of our heads - and that's why we retained our hair up there. This belief was reinforced when the remains of a stone-age hairdresser's shop was found in a Kenyan cave with a sign over the door saying 'Comb As You Are'. No, I just made that bit up.

Persistence hunting must have unleashed profound cultural forces. Increased meat eating would have led to an enormous boost in energy intake, and this would have begun to grow our brain size. One thing led on to another, because these kinds of coordinated hunts would also have needed skills and rudimentary communication to make them work successfully. Someone had to organise and direct the group, develop tracking skills and decide on strategy.

And then, when the prey was killed, there needed to be a recognised leader to keep order and decide on who could eat what, and when. These are capabilities that have come down to us even today: the selection of targets, the procedures to arrive at strategies, organisational talents to meet group needs, and the motivation to persist and endure in achieving our goals. All these things remain deeply human characteristics.

Undoubtedly, the birth of hunting would have unleashed the need for considerable authority and leadership. And developing these led to what anthropologists have coyly termed… the Big Man.

Without language, the Big Man would have had to impose his grunted orders and pointed instructions with pretty unsubtle power plays, and these would almost certainly have involved high levels of violent enforcement. It's probably from these brutal beginnings that our instinctive recognition of hierarchy, and the acceptance we have for leadership in human societies would have come, drummed into our psyches by the sort of quick and unpleasantly rough justice that these sorts would have handed out.

'(Without the Big Man)… human evolution might not revolve
as much around violence, warfare and male dominance, but rather
around sexuality, empathy, caring and cooperation.'
Frans de Waal, *Our Inner Ape*

Nevertheless, why did these early people invest so much time and effort in hunting large animals - as well as taking on the risks of tangling with sharp-toothed threats in things so much bigger than they were? The answer, anthropologists now believe, is that hunting was a terrific way of showing off. Being a visible hero on hunts must have become a key 'mating signal'.

What people regard as alluring might change over time, but what's not in doubt is that deep in our hardwiring are strategies for mate attraction and selection. In those early days of our history, women would have been tied down in the colony with their long pregnancies and child nurturing - while, at the same time, men began to be measured by how aggressively they behaved in a visibly competitive world.

Once one appreciates the respect we developed for hierarchy, or at least for the dangers there are in ignoring authority, then the reasons for these dangerous chases become clearer. That's because the carcasses of large prey would have provided much more meat than the Big Man and his family could have ever eaten on their own. This meant that once they'd had their fill, the boss brigade would have then allowed others to feast, and this kind of largesse is still described by social scientists as 'permitted theft'.

By letting others share in the spoils of his assumed superiority, the Big Man was 'giving' food to the tribe, and in that sense he was trading an assured supply of meat in return for status and authority.

The Eskimo have a saying that 'the best place to store your surplus is in the stomach of another man' and, just as they still evaluate the process, the tribal leader was sending out the most powerful mate signal of all. He was the top dog, he was saying, the person who organised hunts, the man who directed where the community would move to, who kept order, provided for the colony... and he was going to have the best females. And they would want to breed with him.

> **'Seventy thousand years ago, *Homo sapiens* was still an insignificant animal minding its own business in a corner of Africa. In the following millennia it transformed itself into the master of the entire planet and the terror of the ecosystem.'**
> **Yuval Noah Harari, *Sapiens***

So where are we by now? We're up on two legs, running and hunting, accepting authority, dividing our labour, pair bonding, and inventing selective breeding. But we're still pretty dim... so what could change that?

Where was the next great revolution going to come from - and how would it grow our intelligence?

How we became the masters.

CHAPTER TWO

THESE EARLY HOMO SPECIES WERE MAKING PROGRESS. BUT HOW DID THE NEXT GREAT REVOLUTION MAKE OUR BRAINS GROW TO THREE TIMES THE SIZE THEY'D ORIGINALLY BEEN?

Around 1893 Rudyard Kipling had begun to borrow heavily from Indian folk fables when he produced his two volumes of autobiographical allegory called *The Jungle Book*. He referred to it as a 'beast tale' and he was to explain later what this meant when he wrote: '… most of the native hunters in India today think pretty much along the lines of an animal's brain.' In it, he famously describes how his alter-ego, the man-child Mowgli, is taught the laws of the jungle by a black panther called Bagheera.

In the story, Mowgli has been raised by wolves after he'd become lost in the Indian jungle, something that literary commentators have always seen as a parallel with the abandonment that Kipling felt when he was sent back to England for his education.

At the outset of the book, Mowgli and his parents are attacked by a tiger, Shere Khan, and to save the boy's life, his father makes the beast retreat with a burning tree branch. Kipling writes that fire terrified the wild animals so much that none of them would even call it by its proper name. Instead, he says, they '… invented a hundred ways of describing it'. So frightening and yet alluring was it to them that they regarded it as man's unique gift.

Bagheera's name for it is the 'Red Flower' and he instructs Mowgli to steal a smouldering pot from a village. The boy brings it back and Bagheera then tells him to confront the Council of Animals. When they're assembled Mowgli shouts at them: '… this thing will die if I do not give it things to eat!' And, with a flourish, he '… thrust his dead branch into the fire until the twigs lit and crackled, and whirled it above his head among the cowering wolves.'

'Thou art the master', said Bagheera in an undertone.

And so Kipling uses the allegory to describe how fire allowed us to become the masters of our surroundings, and to gain dominion over the other animals. Fire became the second of the great revolutions, and it was to shape and wildly reinforce our evolutionary progress. It would also greatly deepen the role of the Big Man.

We hardly invented it, of course, as it's a natural occurrence in a place as hot as the equator. Trees get hit by lightning, and the brush on the savannah can ignite for all sorts of reasons. But the trick that these early stone-age men managed to pull off was the same as Mowgli's… they were able to *control it*.

When did this first happen? The earliest evidence of scorched hearths goes back as long ago as 1.5 million years, even though most experts don't think that fires would have been used on a regular basis until about 300,000 years ago.

Its benefits completely changed the way we developed. Fire extended daylight, it reduced attacks from wild animals, and the smoke would have discouraged stinging insects. It also kept people warm, and this was undoubtedly the catalyst that allowed tribes to migrate to cooler regions. And it would certainly have given a focus to the social group, and no doubt allowed the Big Man to throw his weight around here as well, laying down the law about who could sit where, be closest to the flames, be upwind of the smoke and so on.

'Look at the man who thought of fire. He could have made an absolute fortune… he should have patented it. Every time anybody lit a fire they'd have had to pay him a royalty. But being a rather primitive person he didn't think of that.' Peter Cook

But what fire also did was to bring another outsourcing breakthrough to our cultural evolution, because it led to *cooking*. This was the breakthrough that created what anthropologists refer to as the 'stomach outside the stomach.' Foods that hominids hadn't previously been able to digest like tubers and wheat-like wild grasses now became staples; complex carbohydrates could suddenly be turned into starchy foods, and meat would now provide far more energy in its cooked state than it ever did when raw. Parasites and bacterial pathogens were also killed by the heat, as were the poisons that had made eating seeds so dangerous.

But most importantly, it takes far less energy to digest cooked food. This key fact allowed the stomach to become smaller… and the brain to become larger. Even in modern man the brain is barely 3% of our body weight, yet it costs us 25% of our energy intake to run it, even at a standstill. The early genera of hominids had been chimp-like in that they spent up to five hours a day chewing their food. Now, with this new kind of energy source they only needed one.

By cooking our food before we ate it, our brains began to grow at an enormous rate. Scientists believe that on average we probably tripled its size from the 400 millilitres of *Australopithecus* (roughly the same capacity as the great apes) to the 700 ml in *Homo erectus*, and then the 1,400 ml or so of you and me. Well OK, more you than me.

Once the brain started expanding, a kind of virtuous circle then set in with problems being increasingly puzzled over and solved, and the formation of the earliest forms of social structures. Things like planning, basic communication, and other more advanced cognitive functions, all began to make the hominids now emerging progressively different to their ape forebears. Some anthropologists also think that the importance of fire led to females adding another way of judging males to their previous criteria: by their ability to defend food stocks.

> **'I believe the transformative moment that gave rise to the genus *Homo*, one of the great transitions in the history of life, stemmed from the control of fire and the advent of cooked meals.'**
> **Richard Wrangham, *Catching Fire: How Cooking Made Us Human***

But when did these early people use the new technology to leave Africa and then evolve down to our *H. sapiens* forebears? The answer, as so often, is both complicated and shrouded in academic disagreement. But amongst the confusion, the bit that doesn't seem to be in any doubt is that some *H. erectus* (sometimes also rather confusingly muddled in with *H. ergaster*) first migrated around 1.8 million years ago. This has been arrived at because of fossil discoveries in SE Asia from roughly that period of Peking man, and the Indonesian islands (Java man). There was even a dwarf-like bunch (*H. floresiensis*) who were seemingly marooned on one of the Lesser Sunda Islands called Flores, and who have rather humiliatingly been termed 'Hobbit man'.

Whether these early travellers made it to Europe is unclear. What seems more likely is that if there were any pioneers they must have become extinct, because modern man doesn't seem to have evolved from a dispersal as early as this, but rather from separate species that would leave Africa much later. These migrations are now thought to have happened around 270,000 years ago; but if this is right then, once again, any descendents of this line are thought to have petered out as well.

There was then a mass dispersal around 130,000 years ago; but the most significant wave seems to have been as recently as 70,000 years… and it's from this last lot that most of us are probably descended.

How did the early explorers leave? Apparently the most likely place was where the Horn of Africa now sticks out opposite the coast of Yemen at the bottom of the Red Sea. The water level would have been much lower at the time, and the migrants might have simply walked across or island hopped over to the Arabian Peninsula. From there they moved eastwards towards Asia, and by 50,000 years ago they're reckoned to have migrated as far as Australia.

But what about nearer home? Nobody's too sure. No fossils have ever been found of *H. erectus* in Western Europe, and the branch that led down to us was probably an intermediate bunch who were responsible for bloodlines that extended as far as Siberia (*H. denisova*) and Germany (*H. heidelbergensis*). And it was probably from this European strain that a bulky and lumbering species emerged in the Neander valley, east of Düsseldorf.

These Neanderthals were a successful and, in many ways, sophisticated people that hunted game and fished with hooks, sewed hide clothes, painted in caves and buried their dead. And from the size of their skulls they appear to have had roughly the same brain capacity as us - and must have rubbed along with our own ancestors once or twice because geneticists reckon we have something like 1-2% of Neanderthal DNA in our gene pool.

They're thought to have become extinct about 40,000 years ago, possibly because they were outcompeted by *H. sapiens* (they certainly couldn't run as fast as we could and were therefore less proficient as hunters) or maybe they simply failed to adapt at the end of the last Ice Age.

> **'Neanderthal people were collateral cousins, perhaps already living in Europe while we emerged in Africa… in other words, we are an improbable and fragile entity, fortunately successful after precarious beginnings as a small population, not the predictable end result of a global tendency.**
> Stephen Jay Gould, *The Structure of Evolutionary Theory*

And us, *Homo sapiens*? Where do we come in? Well, the generally accepted theory is that we probably go back through *H. heidelbergensis* to *H. erectus* and from there all the way to Africa, originally dispersing in the third great migration wave and then spreading throughout a world in which landmasses were far more connected than they are now. They'd have surged eastwards pretty successfully, and it was from there that they reached the Americas around 17,000 years ago, probably over what was then an ice bridge joining Asia to Alaska.

From what biologists can tell, these people looked a lot like us and were probably driven to their global migrations by natural climate changes that led to food resources becoming stressed. But while fresh regions were usually good news for them… it was invariably bad news for any ecosystem that they encountered. Sad to say, our early ancestors weren't thoughtful ecologists, and however much people might wish to paint them as noble savages, living innocently in harmony with their surroundings, they were anything but that.

In fact, they made terrible immigrants. Tribes were ferocious and violent. And their lust for hunting large animals led them to wildly overkill any megafauna they encountered. The idea of tomorrow's needs, never mind future generations, seems to have been completely absent.

Sadly, they'd already been guilty of the same vandalism in Africa. By the time the later emigrations had started, they'd already reduced the average size of mammals there to half what it was in other parts of the world. And that was only the warm up act. In as little as a few thousand years after their arrival in Australasia, for example, early man had slaughtered so widely that mammal and reptile weights dropped precipitously to a tenth of the size they'd been before we'd arrived. Those that hung on were the lucky ones. In total, twenty-three of the twenty-four Australian species that had weighed over a thousand pounds were driven to extinction.

Countless numbers of vast flightless birds, terrestrial crocodiles, marsupial lions, giant kangaroos and enormous wombat species disappeared in an evolutionary blink. New Zealand suffered the same fate, with as many as nine species of the flightless moa bird disappearing forever. These could grow to be over twelve feet tall, but they proved to be no match for the slaughter tactics of the Polynesian migrants.

Similarly, when early humans first entered the Americas, they found a greater diversity of large animals than even exist in Africa today. How they must have licked their lips - and large populations of such things as mammoths, giant sloths, dire wolves, stag-moose, cave lions, massive bison and short-faced bears that would have collectively taken something like thirty million years to evolve, were now brought to extinction within a couple of thousand years of man's arrival.

South America was the same, teeming with camel-like creatures, giant armadillos, long-snouted llamas, monster anteaters and colossal 4,000-pound bears. But our ancestors went through them like the proverbial hot knife. Of the sixty genera of large animals that existed when man first appeared there, fifty were driven to extinction.

'As humans migrated out of Africa, a wave of extinction of large-bodied mammals followed. Our finding that 125,000 years ago, body size in Africa was much smaller than you would expect. By 1.6 million years ago, early hominins were eating meat and became better predators as we were evolving and emigrating. By the time *Homo sapiens* got into the Americas, they had sophisticated long-range hunting weapons, so extinctions became more rapid and more targeted towards larger-bodied mammals.'
Professor Felisa Smith, *University of New Mexico, Science.*

H. sapiens certainly wasn't turning out to be as wise as his name would suggest. Now armed with spear throwing techniques to add to hunting strategies honed over the millennia, they reduced the weight of American mammals from an average of over two hundred pounds to the seventeen it is today. Three quarters of the continent's large species disappeared. In total, worldwide, we were responsible for ninety separate genera that had averaged more than a hundred pounds vanishing without leaving any descendants. Using only basic implements, these early people were responsible for wiping out half of the world's thousand pound plus animals.

But why did they hunt with such unthinking savagery? One can only assume the answer is... because they could. Their staggering wastefulness and lack of understanding of animal husbandry, or of any sense of forward planning about where their next meal would come from, led them to annihilate entire genera and species.

Along the way they drove out predatory competition, upset the natural balance, brought about geographic range shifts and slashed their way through wildlife, killing them with disease if they didn't with their hunting skills.

> '*Homo sapiens* holds the record among all organisms for driving
> the most plant and animal species to extinctions. We have the dubious
> distinction of being the deadliest species in the annals of life.'
> Yuval Noah Harari, *From Animals Into Gods*

Tipping points would have been reached very quickly. As the palaeontological researcher, Advait Jukar of the Smithsonian says: 'It doesn't take a lot to make a species go extinct. Humans don't need to go out and kill every last individual; all you need is a stressed population and just enough hunting pressure to keep the fertility rate below replacement levels. Eventually, the population will collapse.'

Should we condemn our ancestors too greatly? Hmm, I wonder. Man has always been an anxious and jumpy creature, hawk-eyed to danger, neurotic about his food supply, and hardwired for pessimism. When an excess of food is available we just gorge ourselves on it, eating far more than we need, almost as if we had a different kind of metabolism that could store the surplus energy.

You'd think we'd learn, but we're just the same now: many of us are overweight, most of us continue to cram it in, still as tense about our survival as we were tens of thousands of years ago. We may be living in enormous comfort with everything around us and the money to buy it, yet we still seem to be every bit as insecure about food as when we were out on the savannah all those millenia ago.

But if that's where we're similar to these early people, then we were completely different on another crucial measure. That's because these ancestors of ours were astonishingly slow to realise that they could *improve* things. They spent, for example, over a million years using exactly the same type of stone axe. This, along with their other basic tools, didn't advance in any way whatsoever. Why not? After all, it's a feature of our own lives that innovation leads to virtually everything improving over time. So why didn't these ancient people produce better solutions?

Anthropologists are convinced that the key developmental stimulus they lacked was language. Without language people can't share their views and collectively bring about change. Not only that, but what was the point? There wasn't much to reward the efforts of brainy individuals.

The flipside of not searching for outsourced solutions was that communities would have been very stable. Strong social ties were increasingly being laid down, largely because the Big Man would have wanted it this way.

And he'd have instinctively kept a lid on new ways of doing things because any beneficial changes to the tribe's way of life that hadn't come from him would have undermined his authority. What he said was law - and if he decided on something then the rest of his clan would have had to follow him.

Strangely enough, though, these colonies had long ago settled down into having very small numbers in their populations... and no more. Academics now widely assume that this stems from a deep-seated human instinct to protect the social order from the tensions and splits that can threaten its stability.

Most notably, the British anthropologist and evolutionary psychologist, Robin Dunbar, has suggested that there's a 'cognitive limit' that represents a relationship between brain size and colony scale (what's become known as 'Dunbar's number') and which sets a ceiling to how many people can maintain stable social links. This, he says, has led to the '150 Person Rule' that describes how many individuals any of us can know really well and relate to. Even to this day, this sort of figure seems to be the limit at which companies, military units and even group friendships become strained.

Social scientists will point to the comparisons between early and modern man when they say that even present day hunter-gatherer communities have a natural limit of around 150 members. The same number persisted right into the Middle Ages as well, at a time when most villages would have had a church that fitted this number of worshipers.

It's persevered right down to modern man, too. Even though we're citizens of the world now, connected to countless billions through the internet, the number most of us have in our speed dialling lists remains pretty close to the colony size of ancient tribes. How insinctive it seems, that there are only so many relationships we can comfortably manage.

So where are we by now? Millions of years have passed, *H. sapiens* has arrived, we're walking, running, hunting, cooking, our brains have grown mightily, we have tools, social structures and the new horizons that have come from migration. But something's still missing, something that will put rocket fuel into our cultural development.

We still needed to communicate, to discuss things, to learn from others, to influence, and to be influenced... we needed language.

CHAPTER THREE

FEW PEOPLE WOULD ARGUE WITH THE IDEA THAT LANGUAGE WAS WHAT SET HUMANS APART FROM OTHER ORGANISMS. IT'S MAN'S UNIQUE ATTRIBUTE, AND ACQUIRING IT CHANGED EVERYTHING. BUT HOW DID IT COME ABOUT? AND WHAT WERE THE CHANGES THAT ARRIVED WITH THIS THIRD REVOLUTION THAT MEANT WE COULD NOW THINK AND PLAN?

When Georgio Vasari was writing his *Lives of the Artists* back in the middle of the 16th century he described how the great Florentine sculptor, Donatello, had been a fussy perfectionist, little given to fake modesty. But, Vasari relates, even he could be defeated. Apparently, when he was finishing up what his contemporaries regarded as the greatest of his masterpieces - a statue of a bald-headed biblical prophet - Donatello would become so transfixed by his own mastery that he'd be overheard muttering to it: 'Speak, damn you, speak!'

> **'Wherever humans have gone in the world, they have carried with them two things, language and fire... Darwin himself considered these the two most significant achievements of humanity.'**
> **Jerry Adler, *Smithsonian Magazine***

Who can blame him? Speech is what's placed us humans apart from everything else. Other organisms may have shared our origins as humble bacteria, but the human evolutionary journey has taken millions of years of zigging and zagging until we emerged from the confusion of our various ancestor races to become the sentient creatures we are today. However, none of the lurches that got us where we are can have had the cultural impact of this third great revolution.

Tom Wolfe described our acquisition of language in *The Kingdom of Speech* as '... the attribute of all attributes... what lifts man above the animals', and he goes on to say how the process of developing speech allowed us to turn gestures and uninformed thoughts into structured, memorable words, and from there to '... the creation of an internal self and ego'.

This is the internal self of our consciousness, the ability that allows us to be curious and questioning, creative, imaginative and reflective; to influence others and to have their ideas influence us in turn. It's what leads us to drive innovation and improvement, to share with others and to be cooperative, and by doing this to form bonds between individuals - even with strangers - that dramatically improve our ability to arrive at better solutions. In short, it's what has been so critical to allowing us to make 1+1=3.

> '*Imagination is more important than knowledge, for knowledge
> is limited while imagination embraces the entire world.*'
> Albert Einstein, *Ideas and Opinions*

And it's from language that our appreciation of life flows, our moral purpose and the riches of civilisation: art, religion and philosophy, science and literature. It's our *superpower*, something that when we'd perfected it became a game changer of such importance that it separated us from everything else in Nature.

Yet... very little is known about how it originated. Its own development remains a mystery because the collection of mutations and anatomical changes that led to it would have brought so little evolutionary advantage on their own. It was only when they accidently combined together that the end effects could have been produced.

So, how did it all come about?

There's always been a range of theories, of course, but Darwin was probably having an off day when he put forward his own beliefs in *The Descent of Man* that the ability to articulate complex concepts would have originated with our animal forebears. His conclusion was that we'd evolved speech in the same way that birds copied their songs from each other and that '... signs and gestures, various natural sounds, the voices of other animals and man's instinctive cries' somehow joined up to draw the roadmap for the speech revolution.

Other early biologists steered well clear of the subject, regarding it as too tricky or trivial. Institutions such as The Linguistic Society of Paris, for example, banned all debate on it. Many others simply regarded it as not being something for serious study.

Yet having an ability to communicate would have been a vital step in man's development. In the harsh conditions of our early years in Africa, for example, calls and signs would have given us a real survival advantage. Steven Pinker speculated on this in his book *Natural Language and Natural Selection* when he suggests that gestures, grunts and cries could have evolved into intricate patterns over time as people put them together into recognisable combinations. This advance, he believes, would have become of great importance in the precarious world of the hunter-gatherer, and that improvements in communication would have played a major role in making the colony more secure.

Verbal language, of course, depends on the mechanics of fluent articulation… but where did that come from? Were we innately able to do it? You'd be surprised. Not only were we actually incapable, but the evolutionary steps that got us to that point were more like giant leaps. That's because we needed to combine the processing power that was now coming from our growing brains, then to add in an operating system that could only have emerged from chance genetic mutations, and somehow to make it all possible with the entirely new hardware that was available as our anatomy altered.

So, what happened?

First, our structures had been changing for millions of years, not only in our legs and torsos but in our faces and necks as well. Our mouths had been getting smaller and our throats becoming longer as the intricate operation in the region under our heads became more and more complex.

Like other mammals we'd had the same brilliant mechanism that made sure we could breathe and swallow at the same time, but humans being humans, we now wanted to eat our eggs and bacon at breakfast, talk about the weather, keep breathing while we did so… and still not choke to death.

Our bodies started evolving a solution to this by developing a larynx that works like a valve, opening and closing to let air in and out. When it's shut, food goes down to where it should, and hopefully doesn't go hurtling into our lungs.

The immensely complicated organisation of all these different bits depends on a tiny horseshoe shaped bone called the hyoid that's positioned in the neck at roughly the point where the chin comes in. This provides the structural apparatus that connects up and coordinates the network of muscles that branch out to the tongue, the floor of the mouth, the larynx, the pharynx and the epiglottis.

Where did the hyoid come from? Amazingly enough, anatomists think it could have been a leftover bit from when we were marine creatures, and that it evolved from the cartilage of the lower part of the second gill. Other animals may also have versions of it, but its structure is unique to us humans and, remarkably, it's the only bone in the body that isn't attached to any other. This makes it one of the first places suspicious criminal pathologists look when they're carrying out a post-mortem... if it's broken, the person's been strangled.

Anyway, at some point in our history this whole delicate mechanism dropped down our throats. Weird. But why? Nobody's too certain, but perhaps the most widely accepted theory for what became known as the 'laryngeal descent', is that it happened when we got up on two legs and gravity set in.

What it led to, though, was both good news and bad news. The good bit was that we'd somehow developed a voice box that worked in combination with our smaller mouths to give us a wider range of sounds. The bad was... that we could now have food going down the wrong way as we used it. This led to us having to learn a few behavioural tricks to get us round the problem, not least of which is simply to take care of the process when we're eating.

But all this kit is still positioned high up in the throats of newborn babies, and it's for this reason that they can only be fed liquids in their early weeks. Around the time they're three months' old, it starts moving downwards and you can tell this is happening when their little voices change from 'waah waah' shrieks to 'goo goo' gurgles. That's just the beginning, and the descent process isn't completed until they're well into their fourth year.

What was the evolutionary advantage of all this? Well, very little it would seem, arguably the opposite. If the laryngeal drop now put our lives in danger when we were eating, then there had to have been some kind of balancing benefit or we'd have positively selected mutations that found a way around the problem. Since we didn't, the implication can only be that speech made the risk worthwhile.

> 'As our larynxes descended, we were able to make sounds with our mouths in new and far more expressive ways. Verbal language soon overtook physical gesturing as the primary means of communication for all humans except Italians.'
> John Stewart, *EARTH: A Visitor's Guide to the Human Race*

Voices were now capable of a wide range of sounds and the hyoid was critical to controlling the babble. Men's tone, in particular, became lower but the price we chaps paid for this was that our dropped larynx now protruded as a prominent Adam's apple. The dangerous exposure this brought to such a sensitive organ must have been worth it in evolutionary terms because having a big, deep voice is something zoologists believe could have become a mate-signalling device. This is likely, they say, because not only does it indicate higher testosterone levels, but in the natural world, the louder the roar, the larger the animal.

But if the lungs, throat, voice box and mouth combo was now in place, did that mean that we had the ability to speak? Not necessarily. Although it all meant we could range from deafening bellows to throaty whispers, we still had to become better at making sense of the racket we could produce. This tricky stage has led linguists to think that we probably started out by just stringing together calls and grunts into mutually recognisable patterns before meaningful language came along.

What was still needed for us to have careers as livestock auctioneers, however, was a new kind of brain software that could control the process - an operating system that would make us capable of fast, intelligible and sophisticated language. And this didn't come along until about 50,000 years ago, when a couple of mutations occurred to a protein coding gene in our brains called FOXP2.

Now, FOXP2 is actually present in other mammals as well, and as with us it's critical for proper brain and lung development. But the mutations that took place in *H. sapiens* somehow worked together with everything else to produce a unique breakthrough that wasn't shared with other organisms. Nor, indeed, was it present in our ancestors. What did these mutations add up to? They gave us a new and extraordinary control over the muscles of the throat and mouth… and it was this that now made rapid articulation possible.

If ever there was a case of deleterious mutations leading to positive outcomes then this was it. Suddenly all those underutilised voice boxes could be put to more refined use, and decorous pursuits were now possible like declaiming poetry, singing arias and shouting at call centres.

'I personally believe we developed language because of our deep inner need to complain.'
Jane Wagner, *The Search for Signs of Intelligent Life in the Universe*

How did researchers find out about the role of the FOXP2 gene? It was only discovered fairly recently, and in the saddest way imaginable, when doctors were trying to work out why fourteen members of the same large London family were each suffering from such profound verbal dyspraxia that they were incapable of articulate speech. Otherwise they were fine.

The culprit that separated these poor people from the fifteen others in their family that could speak normally was found to be the FOXP2 gene. From this, scientists were then able to see its importance in controlling the neural circuitry in the brain that's so necessary for complex language.

Buddhists call the hyoid the 'Buddha bone' because it brought about speech. Biologists call FOXP2 the 'grammar gene' because it unleashed complex expressions. Now the two things combined with the ability to regulate breathing patterns, and our language attribute set up home in a region of the brain called Broca's area, named after the French neuro-anatomist who discovered it. Injure that, doctors now know, and we can lose the power of speech.

But understanding the action of the FOXP2 gene also now led scientists to suggest some further insights. The protein that it produces is, for example, more active in women than in men, and this is believed to give them faster and deeper language skills. Rather more debatable, though, is the claim that because women have something like thirty percent more of it present in their brains than men, they're inclined to be more talkative and emotionally articulate.

So, when did a recognisable form of language get underway? Once again, there are only clues to go on, but that's never stopped heated debates breaking out among linguists. For many years, there seemed to be general agreement that it had evolved in a Darwinian way, and that our thoughts had been slowly shaped into coherent language over long periods by what's called a 'continuity approach'.

Darwin's alter ego, Alfred Russel Wallace, for example, saw the evolution of the human brain not as the result of language, but as the stimulus for it. This was because our creation of consciousness, morality, culture and all our other 'higher' attributes meant that these self-generated qualities were communication-based, rather than the products of natural selection.

For a long time, the majority of academics in the field followed the beliefs of the Swiss semiotician and philosopher, Ferdinand de Saussure, in what was known as 'structural linguistics'. This approach said that language could be broken down into a hugely complicated symbolic system in which units of communication acquired identities and had dual meanings, depending on both the signifier and the signified, and was largely generated by our behavioural psychology.

Other theories that were being put forward included the idea that speech began with simple imitations, the modification of tool-use sounds (Broca's area is next to the region of the brain employed during flint knapping), from mother comforting expressions, or even from other kinds of evolutionary adaptations.

The Secrets of Life - Book Two

Perhaps the most widely held belief, however, was that verbal structures developed out of gesturing because both forms of communicating use similar neural pathways in the brain. This led biologists to think that manual gestures both triggered speech - and then supplemented it.

At base, most opinions revolved around a 'refinement model' that suggested the language process had been created in the same manner as any other kind of learning procedure - by trial and error, repetition and rewards. In this way, sophisticated speech had evolved by people giving words to their experiences, and then building up meanings and sentence structures by combining them in a progressively more organised way.

Then in 1957 everything changed. A young Harvard educated academic called Noam Chomsky published a book entitled *Syntactic Structures* that threw all the linguistic cards in the air, kicked the table away, and chucked his drink over the other players. Language, Chomsky was now saying, wasn't something we'd painfully built up at all. Quite the opposite. In his view it was an *innate attribute*, the result of an evolutionary pathway that had led humans to have a built-in language organ, something that was as fully formed in our brains as our hearts or kidneys were in our bodies.

This was the only explanation Chomsky could see for why, from one generation to the next, we were all able to understand instinctively the principles of syntax. And it was from these natural skills that we communicated with each other. The ability had become embedded in us, he claimed, because our hardwiring was programmed with something he called 'Universal Grammar', a phenomenon that was common to every human, regardless of race or background, and which cut across socio-cultural differences and language orders.

Because it was an inherited characteristic, Chomsky believed that his 'discovery' of the brain's function - what he was now calling a 'Language Acquisition Device' - had advanced far faster in us than the way the 'continuity' theorists had proposed. It was, he claimed, probably in place by 50,000 years ago.

In addition, he concluded that the LAD had developed as the result of a chance mutation in just one individual, but because it was so advantageous and genetically transmitted, it was now present in all humans. It was this genetic change that marked us out as separate from other animals.

Universal Grammar was the product of the LAD, according to Chomsky, and this was why children could start talking so early, and why they had such an astonishingly quick grasp of structure, as well as an understanding of the difference between noun and verb use.

It was also the reason why they were able to understand and articulate entirely new sentences and novel expressions, including ones that they might never have heard from others. This could be the only explanation, he said, for why they were able to overcome the gap between what they could have picked up from others, and the linguistic knowledge they developed so extraordinarily quickly… a gap that had always troubled academics and was known as the 'poverty of stimulus' problem.

'Do you imagine he could be referring to Universal Grammar?'

But what seemed to be the final flourish of evidence for Chomsky's revolutionary theories was that they explained something that linguists call recursion. This is the process of putting one thought inside another to arrive at complex sentence construction. Such an ability would have been impossible for children, he said, without having an inherited skill.

What's an example of recursion? Well, a sentence such as 'Gillie assumed that now Sean's youthful years were over, and his different careers had come to an end, he would buckle down and write the book he'd been talking about for so long' would be impossible without a very specific linguistic mastery. That's because the ideas that are bundled up in a sentence like this are very complicated.

In this example, tucked away inside the thought beginning 'Gillie assumed…', there are a further five concepts, all of them quite distinct. No child, Chomsky said, would be capable of recursive structures without Universal Grammar.

What did the rest of the academic world make of these extraordinary new theories? They had such a different premise to everything that had gone before, and must have seemed so completely counterintuitive, that surely Chomsky would have struggled to have had them accepted?

Seemingly not; academics may have disagreed with some aspects of them, but they came to be wary of academic bun fights. Chomsky was well known as a public bruiser, famous for his far left views and extreme criticisms of US foreign policies, And he was equally uncompromising with fellow linguists who got the wrong side of him.

Instead of appearing to welcome discussion, he would frequently portray his critics, as Stephen Pinker later wrote, as '… stupid or evil, using withering scorn in his rhetoric', and these tactics tended to put off open-minded debate. Chomsky's new school of thought had also attracted a group of loyal disciples, and for many years his beliefs became the generally accepted tenets in the linguistic field.

Then, just as Chomsky's claims had taken root almost overnight, so the wheel turned and they equally suddenly came to be seen as absurd. The reversal arrived out of nowhere, from a complete amateur: an obscure missionary called Daniel Everett who'd been sent by his church to convert a tribe called the Piraha who'd remained hidden deep in the Amazon basin.

Even though his words fell on stony ground and he never actually converted a single one of them, Everett lived with the colony for years and became fluent in their language. The more he spoke it, and the more he came to know the people as individuals, the more convinced he was that instead of speech being innate, it was a purely human invention. Its origins, Everett became increasingly certain, had arisen simply to solve the communication problems present in small societies.

The Piraha, he found, were a contented people, and they had no need for more than three vowels and eight consonants; they had no way of describing numbers or colours, they had a scant regard for creation myths or in any kind of higher being, and they also displayed no wish to talk about either the distant past or an imagined future. Perhaps most significantly, Everett later wrote, there was a total absence of recursion in the way they spoke. They never placed one concept inside another.

He returned from the rainforest convinced that he'd made a series of key anthropological discoveries that had been exposed, he said, because: '… to learn a language you have to think like the people who speak it and… it's hard to think like a stone-age hunter-gatherer.'

What he had to say about the tribe, though, turned the idea of an LAD and Universal Grammar on its head: the Piraha's sentences were short, they got straight to the point, and they had no place for vague concepts of 'truth' in their values. 'Truth… is catching a fish, rowing a canoe, laughing with your children', Everett wrote, and in 2009 he published his findings in a book that summed up the tribe's attitude to life when he used as its title the way they wish each other 'goodnight' … *Don't Sleep, There Are Snakes*. It became a bestseller and went on to deliver a crushing blow to Chomsky's beliefs.

'Either he's wrong', Everett concluded, 'or the Piraha are not human.'

Back and forth went the rows. But by now the academic world had been given powerful reasons to regroup and push back at Chomsky and his cohorts. Everett became something of an academic star, taking on university positions and producing another best-selling book called *How Language Began: The Story of Humanity's Greatest Invention* that further consolidated his continuity theories on the origins of speech. In this, as in his lectures, he set about rubbishing the idea that an innate neural apparatus had created a pre-programmed brain but, in turn, he now startled people with his own novel theory. This was that language had originated with *Homo erectus*, one and a half million years earlier than had previously been thought - and well before the FOXP2 mutation.

> **'All human behaviour, including language, is the working**
> **out of intentions, what our minds are directed towards.'**
> **Daniel Everett, *How Language Began***

His view was not to claim that these early people communicated with sophisticated language but that they, like the Piraha: '… were not incapable of speech, they just would have had different speech.' Everett was now proposing that language had arrived with our larger brains, and developed alongside gestures and intonations to build a recognisable version of spoken communication at an understandable evolutionary pace of some 60,000 generations. Such niceties as grammar and complex sentences would have evolved, he said, not because people particularly cared about their construction, but simply because it was a way of making the users better understood.

And then, weirdly, in 2014 Chomsky and six other heavyweight biologists and linguists jointly penned a piece in the journal *Frontiers of Psychology* that reset the debate. Some opponents even delightedly claimed that they were running up the white flag. 'In the last 40 years', the group wrote, 'there has been an explosion of research into how language began, but… the most fundamental questions about the origin and evolution of our linguistic capacity remain as mysterious as ever.' Oh well, while that seemed to be game over for a lot of their ideas, research and debate into the origins of language are bound to continue.

But whatever the truth may be about how language was first fired up in us… *what were we actually talking about?* What did these stone-age people have to say to each other?

And, possibly more to the point, what were they laying down as rules for living that have descended all the way down to us… shaping along the way, our attitudes, behaviour and cultures?

Before language developed...

CHAPTER FOUR

SO WE'RE LIVING IN COMMUNITIES, HUNTING, FORAGING AND EVEN TRAVELLING. BASIC LANGUAGE HAS TAKEN ROOT... BUT WHAT WERE WE USING IT FOR? AND WHY DO THE ANSWERS TO THIS QUESTION MATTER SO MUCH TO US NOW?

What were these early people talking about? Well, a number of things, it's believed... things that were to make us who we are today and how we've ended up behaving.

And this is because humans found that with language they were able to influence and shape the thinking of another person. Bashing someone on the head might still get them what they wanted, but now people were using their new abilities to communicate observations and judgments - and they were finding that the sheer power of their ideas could achieve the same thing as force.

First, we were surely now giving each other information. Orders, warnings, instructions, names, threats and so on. And these facts must have become central to a growing realisation that improvements were possible if we were given good advice. 'Watch out when its eyes narrow' - might keep you alive with a cornered animal. 'Hit the stone higher up' - could lead to better tools. 'Don't sit in the chief's seat' - would maintain hierarchy. 'Get orf moi land' - could ensure territorial rights (and the grotesquely high levels of violence that enforced it).

And when they began to give each other names, there was doubtless some early joker who came up with the line 'you can call me anything you like, but don't call me late for lunch' that would have kept them rolling round the tribal fire in stitches.

Secondly, though, anthropologists say that we went further than just banging out facts. They believe these early colonies now began to elaborate on life with much more interesting and juicy stuff... because it was at about this point in our evolution that people began to gossip.

The original reason for what remains our favourite occupation was that there's always been a lot of hanging about in hunter-gatherer societies. Keeping an eye out for things like prey appearing, or berries ripening, was a lot less action-critical than the seasonal demands of seeding or reaping that would come later with agriculture. Instead, ways of developing social bonds now became more important, and people began to fill the time in ways we'd probably still recognise.

These days we love our social media and reality television, but they're actually only the latest version of the kind of interest our long-dead ancestors started to show in each other. Just like us, these people were constantly chewing over what they were doing and seeing, what they thought of each other, who was doing what to whom, who was acting in the right way, who was respected, who they rated - and all this gassing added up to a constant reinforcing of the tribe's notion of community, and particularly of its pecking order.

When they're researching the world's remaining hunter-gatherer tribes, anthropologists still see this going on today: 'Phwoar, that Roger! Did you spot how he was ordering the hunters around? He's the right stuff… I wonder if he's thinking of having babies'. Or, maybe: 'I don't know what it is about her but she always seems to find the best berries.' And, most of all: 'I'm glad he's our chief.' Sound familiar? Of course it does - we may think we've progressed, but people are still fascinated by the same kind of things that they were talking about back then.

Gossip has always been riveting. It allows people to swap views and to store up bits of information and opinion they can trade. In those early groups this kind of chatter would have encouraged bonding and relationships, and so built up social networks. Most importantly of all, gossiping about each other would have highlighted the importance of *trust* at a time when people had nothing else to go on but the behaviour they were observing in each other. Nattering on about what they thought of each other would have developed personalities, and the notion of individual identities and reputations.

In his book *Grooming, Gossip and the Evolution of Language*, the British anthropologist, Robin Dunbar, suggests that gossip began as a form of social grooming that took over from the manual scratching and pest removal that early hominids performed, and primates endlessly continue to carry out today. As colony numbers settled, he says, vocal grooming became another way of servicing allies and friends, and yet still allowed people to keep both their hands free for other things.

The Secrets of Life - Book Two

By doing this, Dunbar concluded that language was fundamentally a form of social behaviour that began being used in small communities - up to his 'limit' of around 150 individuals - in which sentences became tidbits of gossip. These 'units' were ideal because they contained subtleties of meaning and were peppered with verb words that described what people did, or what they were going to do... and this all resulted in a terrific way of conveying information about what was going on in their tiny societies.

Why was this information so necessary? It was because humans had yet to completely sublimate their natural drives for survival and reproducing, and knowing who would make a good mate, who could be trusted and who was a cheat, who hated whom and who could be a danger, all these questions and others were the sorts of issues that were even more important to one's safety than how to avoid snakes or split stones.

But, thirdly, language now began to feed and nourish an entirely new human construct - because it was about this time that primitive peoples gave birth to imagination.

Whether images were being conveyed by the new form of pictorial art or by the power of storytelling, the symbolism and emotional charges that were being fed into prehistoric brains must have been incredibly exciting. People were now able to describe fantasies, summon up images, echo profound fears and hopes, dream up gods and legends, describe a narrative that linked outside forces to their own lives, and to create myths that explained where they'd come from, and what their roles in life should be.

Gods, spirits, fictions and lore must have all started appearing about now, and these powerful concepts played a crucial role in people's desire to give their lives a special meaning. They were also used to elevate themselves above the things they saw around them. As Robin Dunbar wrote in *Human Evolution*: 'There are probably two key aspects of culture that stand out as uniquely human. One is religion and the other is storytelling.'

> **'We are storytelling animals and cannot bear to**
> **acknowledge the ordinariness of our daily lives.'**
> **Stephen Jay Gould, *The Flamingo's Smile***

Our inner lives began to develop as these fictions took root. And with our imaginations came our unique ability to hold the kind of deep beliefs that could secure cooperative relationships with non-family members. They also contributed to our need to have power structures that satisfied a wish for natural superiority.

The idea that if people were better organised they could become more efficient - ideally arranged into hierarchies and led by a Big Man (and his elite cronies) - was laid down about now as one of the foundation stones for how society should be structured.

These leaders, in turn, would have whipped up a love of group identity for the community, mystical explanations of their pecking order, a hatred of outsiders and strangers, and for pretty well anything else that wasn't in the colony and therefore wasn't under their control.

> 'A myth is a way of making sense in a senseless world. Myths
> are narrative patterns that give significance to our existence.'
> Rollo May, *Man's Search for Himself*

And it wasn't just talk. Because with the logical processes that language now provided, we also began to think about ourselves. Our inner voices were unleashed for self-reflection, introspection and the endless attempts to work out things like our purpose and being. For the first time we became conscious of who we were as individuals. Descartes' idea of needed 'I think, therefore I am' now took on profound meaning as early humans began to career around, trying to handle what must have been a disturbing new power.

At last, it seemed, we could now explain things to our questioning minds, and to think about how we could develop meaningful relationships with others. Our initial, tentative steps at wondering at the mysteries of the world and each other must have meant that the blank slate of our minds, the *tabula rasa*, would have been filling up pretty quickly with whatever seemed to make sense to our individual and collective imaginations.

For philosophers, the way this process got going was another of those 'chicken and egg' arguments that are so often used when debating the origins of human life. Some favour the 'language first' idea which says that imagination and self-awareness were only made possible once a colony of people had found a way of communicating with each other. The American writer, Joan Didion, for example, sums this up in *Slouching Towards Bethlehem* when she says: 'The ability to think for oneself depends upon one's mastery of the language.'

Others argue for a second, 'thought first' approach, in which the mistily understood concepts and pictures that whirred around people's heads couldn't be explained or communicated until they'd developed structured language. This must

'Whaaaat?'

have been rather like the baffled look one sees on the faces of little babies when they're staring around themselves, obviously taking things in and yet trying to work out what's going on without the tools to do it. As Ferdinand de Saussure himself said: 'Without language, thought is a vague, uncharted nebula.'

And with thought came memory and experience, the ability to recall events and then project forward to what might happen in the future - and therefore the ability to employ decision-making to one's best advantage. We learnt, in other words, to *plan*.

Language allowed people to discuss different ways of doing things, to weigh up the consequences of their actions, and then to select what they thought would be the best outcomes. Maybe it was around now that we actually began to deserve the '*sapiens*' tag? Perhaps all these new qualities of ours added up to a kind of wisdom?

What's extraordinary, though, is just how quickly everything must have happened. After a literally stuttering start, humans would have progressed in an incredibly short period of time from a narrow range of animal reactions, to refining their capacity for considered decisions.

I guess this was the beginning of our great journey to evolve the unique attribute we have of 'culture': a way of doing things that a society would develop as an agreed way to live, something that each member would understand and take pride in. Cultures were unifiers, they underpinned behaviour and they were a source of self-respect. It was doubtless something that made one superior to the way that other tribes lived - all those barbarians who didn't even speak a language that anyone half decent could understand.

Of course, these were exactly the kind of group beliefs and attitudes that the Big Man was encouraging, and laying down as his to enforce. Added together, they'd have enhanced his right to rule, and established the conviction in his followers' minds that only he had the intelligence and insights to see what ordinary men could not. It was this that gave him the authority to tell others what to think.

But what was happening in all those embryonic minds as they were taking in the massive amounts of information and attitudes that would shape their thought patterns and outlooks? It was the brain at work, coding itself, firing up the electro-chemical connections of dendrites and stimulating them through synapses to neurons - a process of programming that was laying down our 'hard wiring'.

> 'According to the anthropologist, Joe Heinrich, humans learn skills from each other by copying prestigious individuals, and they innovate by making mistakes that are very occasionally improvements - that is how culture evolves.'
> Matt Ridley, *The Rational Optimist*

This thought process, however, has always been an unfinished business. Why's that? It's because the network of neurons that are buzzing round our brains are constantly being modified by whatever it is that we're pondering on, or hearing, or experiencing. This means that our brains are in a perpetual state of change that biologists have named neuroplasticity, a process by which our internal wiring adjusts and alters itself to deal with whatever the latest stimuli are to be hitting it.

As Marcus Chown describes in *What A Wonderful World*: 'The brain is a computer but it is a remarkable kind of computer. Whereas a silicon-based computer carries out a task according to a program fed to it by a human being, the brain has no external program. It is a self-programming computer.'

> 'Since the dawn of civilisation, *Homo sapiens* has become a self-programmable species.'
> Alex Vikoulov, *The Origins of Us*

Although I imagine these early *H. sapiens* wouldn't have been much troubled by it, the distinction between what we regard as 'mind' and what we think of as 'consciousness' were now beginning to separate out. What's the difference? Tricky to be precise, but the consensus seems to be that the mind is the result of the brain's constant mental reprogramming, a physical process that can feed back to influence itself, just as it had first been influenced by outside things. In other words, these primitive people began to bring their own experiences and responses into the feedback loop of thinking.

> '**Neuroplasticity is the brain's big secret. Like natural selection in evolution and DNA in genetics, it is an idea so central to understanding the brain that, without it, nothing makes sense. Neuroplasticity explains how new experiences constantly rewire the brain - the ultimate lump of programmable matter.**'
> Marcus Chown, *What A Wonderful World*

Consciousness, however, is a higher process: it is the mind at work, recognising itself yet still self-dependent on carrying out the process. In a sense it transcends the physical steps of programming to create something almost mystical, in that it makes its own existence possible.

Perhaps the Austrian physicist, Erwin Schrodinger, came closest to nailing the inherent vagueness of any definition when he said: 'Consciousness cannot be accounted for in physical terms. For consciousness is absolutely fundamental. It cannot be accounted for in terms of anything else.'

But if stone-age humans had progressed through the power of language to move from their animal pasts to becoming sentient beings, how did the confusion that must have been taking place in their brains, the neuroplasticity that was incorporating new experiences, the separation of their minds from their growing consciousness, the effect of their imaginations and individual thoughts being shaped by group beliefs, the need to sort out whether their internal monologues came from their own thoughts or were a conduit for external gods and spirits... how did this storm of stimuli settle down into the codes of behaviour that everyone was to sign up to?

Most academics seem to suggest two possible answers to this. First, the Big Man was certainly configuring human cultures to fit his own ends. He and his supporters would have been the ones laying down the social norms, and these would have restricted too much individual self-determination or considered decision-making. No doubt he did this by enforcing his views with fairly unpleasant punishments.

The American anthropologists, Peter Richerson and Robert Boyd, for example, have highlighted the way that language would have hugely catalysed the progression to social organisation, and the ways in which it was being influenced by the effects of genetic and cultural evolution. In *The Origin and Evolution of Cultures* they say that: 'Culture completely changes the way that human evolution works, but not because culture is learned.' Instead, they say, behavioural rules were (and are): '...

transmitted from generation to generation and, like genes, they are evolving properties of the population.'

But, secondly, we were developing our behaviour along certain lines because doing this suited us. We were learning what to do and how to think... because we were copying others. We did this because we'd absorbed the lesson that the best way to survive and stay out of trouble was by going along with what successful people seemed to be doing. They were the winners in society - so why not follow their lead?

The Canadian evolutionary biologist, Joseph Heinrich and his wife, Natalie, have long researched the way our cultures become programmed as we do this. In their book *Why Humans Cooperate* they sum this approach up when they say: 'A good imitator can simply observe and learn from other members of his group, thereby taking advantage of the accumulated experience and wisdom of previous generations... by focusing on the healthiest members of his group.'

Language really was the glue that helped the process of successful imitation, and built the bonds of social organisation. Now life wasn't just about oneself - others in the tribe began to matter too. And this was because the growing power of the imagination was beginning to give these prehistoric people an appreciation of *what was going on in the heads of other people*. We think of stone-age man as uncivilised and brutal, but the invention of language would have introduced into their societies what psychologists call 'theory of mind' - the ability we all have to imagine what people other than ourselves are thinking, how they'll be weighing things up, and what they'll be using to base their decisions on.

This was an extraordinary new ability. It allowed us to embark on the realisation that one's actions would have an effect on others, and that we could guess at what conclusions they were coming to. We began to learn the rudiments of sympathy and empathy. We also found that we could use our imaginations to understand how to control others. True, this led us to suppress and bully, but we also learnt how we could shape our own behaviour and strategies to influence others, and therefore how we could get the best out of situations.

We found we could *think ahead*, and so behave and say things that made us better off. And by developing an instinct for predicting what insights another person might arrive at, we learnt the subtleties of dealing with other people. This was a process that led directly to the clan's success, because it also meant we could work out how to maximise the gains that came from the division of labour.

In short, we were learning how to specialise our skills so we could become more attractive to others when it came to all those endless questions about what's the right balance of giving and taking in societies.

But did the blizzard of stimuli that language must have brought unsettle our still-changing brains? Well, it's tempting to be flippant and say 'why not ask a shrink?' Because are we really so different, even today? In terms of evolutionary periods, we've only just arrived as a species, a few tens of thousands of years old, so maybe the ancient conflicts between our instincts and our mental solutions are still too fresh to give us any real sense of comfort. As Sigmund Freud was later to famously observe: 'It is impossible to overlook the extent to which civilisation is built upon a renunciation of instinct.'

'Man can alter his life by altering his thinking.'
William James, *The Principles of Psychology*

But some things did stick. Thoughts might come and go, opinions could change as events alter them, but even the most individual and maverick of us - however empathetic, or however uncaring - has certain core beliefs. These are our articles of faith, if you like, things that are so deeply embedded in our personalities that we regard them as *'natural'*. These are the beliefs that seem so obvious to us that they're almost impossible to separate out from our sense of 'self'.

We all know that's the case… but where do these convictions come from?

How does he do it? It's because he's the meme man.

CHAPTER FIVE

IF THE BRAIN IS IN A CONSTANT PROCESS OF NEUROPLASTIC CHANGE, THEN HOW DID WE EVER CREATE THE RULES THAT UNDERPIN OUR SOCIETIES - BOTH IN THOSE EARLY DAYS AND NOW? DID CERTAIN BELIEFS JUST BECOME SO POWERFUL THAT WE ALL ENDED UP AGREEING TO THEM?

How did some ideas become so fixed in us that they laid down the bedrock of our culture? What was the process that evolved and how, particularly, did we establish the essential bonds that hold our societies together?

Richard Dawkins was among the first biologists to focus on these questions and to propose that some group convictions were so deeply preserved that they were actually being passed down from one generation to the next. In doing this way they were, he said, acting in the same way that genes do in the reproductive process. How can that be? Surely we're born without any beliefs at all?

It was because they play a *complementary* role to our genetic inheritance in our decision-making processes. These core agreements, they say, put down deep roots in our societies, and they've had the effect of creating a largely homogenous outlook among us. They were central to creating our culture, and have given us the rules to live by.

Professor Dawkins termed these fundamental certainties as *memes*: units of non-genetic, yet plainly inherited, information.

Robert Wright was to write about the parallel between memes and our genetic evolution in his book, *Nonzero*. In it he describes the role they play as part of the process of natural selection because: '… natural selection preserves those genes that happen to act as if they were pursuing a strategy. And so it is with memes.'

Memes arrived with language because people found they could now describe the profound beliefs, knowledge, customs and rules that governed their little societies. In this way, they became part of what we began to inherit from previous generations, and were therefore essential factors in our survival strategies. It was how things were done - and everyone signed up to them - or didn't fit in. And they were critical to success. Matt Ridley describes this in *The Rational Optimist* as leading: '… to a whole new kind of evolution going on in us humans - a competition not between genetically different individuals or groups, but between culturally different individuals or groups. One person may thrive at the expense of another, not because he's got better genes, but because he knows or believes something that's of practical value.'

Many biologists now believe that memes can have such power that they behave like an infection, a virus, in the sense that they're absorbed so completely into the hardwiring of the receiver that once they've been established, they can 'parasitise' the person's brain, and completely shape what people believe in.

'But if thought corrupts language, language can also corrupt thought.'
George Orwell, *1984*

Can this really be the case? Well, humans don't start out as entirely blank sheets of paper which others scrawl on. Instead, we're born with natural instincts. We're then brought up to imitate people about how to behave, and what to believe. This is the process of us copying the successful strategies of others and it leads us, of course, to generally hold the same codes of morality and behaviour that we see in other members of our societies. These are the memes that we were, and still are, using to guide our way in life.

But what kind of thoughts and feelings do these memes convey?

Some go to the heart of society - our beliefs about the family, for example, or the value of loyalty, the power of friendships, our admiration for service, our respect for sacrifice and altruism, the need for fairness and justice, the healing power of compassion, our instinctive wariness of strangers and their ideas, the commitment to protect territorial rights, the role of leaders and our need to control them, the importance of moral virtues and, of course, for the sanctity of life itself.

'No amount of data and no mathematical wizardry can prove that it is wrong to murder. Yet human societies cannot survive without such judgements.'
Yuval Noah Harari, *Homo Deus*

Some go to ourselves - a desire for recognition, the willingness to defend ourselves against attack, our ambivalence about personal success, the various ways of mate signalling, our profound wish for happiness, for love, and even as the Buddhists teach, for oblivion.

As to our role in societies, at base we're like other organisms in choosing between a strategy of winning by following the zero sum way of beating other people, or of choosing the opposite strategy of non-zero, and helping other people in a community win - and so winning ourselves. In choosing one of these routes we're acting out the fundamental division of the behavioural strategies that are always present throughout the natural world.

And then some memes go to what many people would regard as imaginary constructs - to the religious beliefs we hold, to the acceptance of hierarchies, to creation myths, the spirit world, dream states and even to the presumption of power.

We think of most of these convictions as completely innate, *obvious*, hardly worthy of discussion. But actually, they're not natural at all, and one has only to look at how diverse memes of this kind can be to realise the extent to which there's so much disagreement, even about the things that one would imagine were inarguable.

What's the difference between the Isil jihadist, for example, convinced that killing a swathe of people in the Great Satan would improve the future of mankind… and an American redneck, who passionately believes that 'nuking' the Middle East would solve everything? Not much would be my conclusion. Yet both are convinced that they're right, leading one to wonder at how completely parasitised their brains must be to hold such extreme, yet opposing opinions.

We might shrug at the narrow outlooks of both these nut jobs… but are we so different ourselves? Don't we all become utterly maddened by people who hold beliefs that oppose our own world views? Hard workers get angry when they see society's takers, honest people are appalled by liars, rule followers tut at the disorderly, and atheists at the religious - to take just some of the more obvious cases. And however relaxed we may think we appear, pretty well every one of us is constantly fretting over other people's opinions that we just *know* are wrong.

Like what? Well, take even the most trivial things. No doubt there have been occasions as you've been reading this book when you've thought: 'hang on, that can't be right!' But are you sure? Or are you simply convinced that this is the case because you were informed by a 'source' you particularly respected, with an idea placed in you so long ago that you can't possibly remember it?

Each of us carries around a collection of these fixed assumptions, and while they might help us structure our views on life, we most certainly don't like having them questioned. Even basic guidelines or simple scientific facts can become things that we just know to be true.

Like what? Well, take a few racing certainties such as: that water conducts electricity, or that we only use 10% of our brain power, or that sugar makes children hyperactive, or that we shouldn't swim after a meal, or even that our hair and nails continue to grow when we're dead. Now how do we feel when we're told that none of these 'facts' is true? Yet each one of them, apparently, stems from a misunderstanding, or is just plain wrong. Try a couple of internet searches for 'science myths debunked' to see what I mean.

Now, do we enjoy having our opinions so roughly thrown in the bin? No, probably not. In fact, we'd probably get cross about it, in spite of things like this being relatively unimportant. But what about rather more central matters such as disagreements about the use of vaccines, or the different views on same sex marriage, or transgender people, or the role of religion in morality, or cultural differences between races, or the importance of national pride, and so on and on? What's going on there? Why do people abandon the idea of measured debate, or the use of evidence to guide discussions, and instead get their knickers in quite such a twist over them?

'People would rather believe than know.'
EO Wilson, *The Meaning of Human Existence*

Hugo Mercier and Dan Sperber examined the phenomenon of these kinds of utter convictions in their book, *The Enigma of Reason*, when they argued that memes must have developed in early hunter-gatherer societies as a socio-linguistic way of shaping the 'architecture of human reasoning'. It was these, they say, that accounts for the appetite we have for the profound beliefs that remain with us still.

In their book they go on to illustrate just how deeply these views can be held. They describe a number of psychological experiments in which respondents are confronted by the proof that they'd been misled, and are then interviewed about how they now feel. Bad is the general answer. It isn't even uncommon, in some cases, to experience 'physical pain' when people have to face up to being in the wrong. The price they can pay for having their memes disturbed is to undergo, what the authors describe as: 'hurt, literally'.

When they were working on the Treaty of Versailles, for example, John Maynard Keynes famously described the American President, Woodrow Wilson, as: 'once bamboozled, very hard to unbamboozle'. Most of us still have quite a lot of the Wilson certainties in our lives.

If we find it hard to shake off these memes as individuals, then it's almost impossible to do so once they've become embedded in the 'group mind' of a society. We cling to beliefs for dear life, seeing them as almost the definition of our principles, and critical to what our cultures stand for.

It's hardly surprising that some races and nations can feel so united by such things, adopting a uniform acceptance of their history or cultures, having collective views, and being prone to develop a victim mentality if these convictions are ever derided or questioned. Sometimes this can become so central to a population's sense of self-worth that entire nations can go wildly off the rails if they feel they're not respected, or believe they've been unfairly treated.

On the other hand, memes are also riddled with contradictions and overlap. We tend, for instance, to respect the universal right to freedom of worship these days, and look back on the days of religious persecution as cruel and brutish. Yet our current lack of prejudice is arguably even more bizarre than bigotry, because its implication is that we think believers must be simple-minded or plain wrong in holding their views. If there are so many different religions, we seem to be saying (whether they're monotheist, polytheist or humanist), then some faiths, by definition, must be fantasies, and their followers must have been misled when they allowed them into their heads.

Alternatively, if we're convinced about our own beliefs - but these run counter to other faiths and their teachings - the inference has to be that we're patronising their followers with our tolerance because we secretly think they're mistaken for believing them. After all, they can't all be right.

This ability for us to hold two opposing views in our minds - what psychologists call 'cognitive dissonance' - must have arrived at around the time language was allowing this sort of nuanced reasoning to be at odds with our memes. Have we ever truly come to terms with it? The scale of the counselling industry would suggest we haven't.

But aren't all these memes just a posh new way of saying attitudes? What's the big deal about them? Scientists insist they're much more than that. First, they say, it's because memes go far deeper into our hardwiring than our changeable opinions would ever do.

Secondly, they differ from attitudes because they're not generated by ourselves, but are passed on to us by others. In doing this, evolutionary theorists are claiming that the ideas act like an invading force, taking over our brains and shaping what we regard as natural. It's *other* people who are doing this to us, just as we, in turn, will probably pass on our own beliefs to new receivers.

Susan Blackmore highlighted the differences in her book, *The Meme Machine*, when she wrote that memes illustrate exactly the same three characteristics of replication that genes do. Like them, she proposed, they copy with great accuracy. Then they have what she calls 'fecundity' in that they become widely spread. And last, that they're long lived.

Professor Blackmore's hypothesis is that their origins go back to when tool-making techniques were widely shared and copied, and that they then became catalysed as we developed language. Once embedded in us, a similar kind of selection pressure to gene transfer favoured their longevity because people imitated what appeared to be good choices. Increasingly these decisions were then seen as based on individual reason and intelligence.

But are biologists really suggesting that these profound ideas are heritable? Are they saying we're actually born with cultural concepts in our make-up? One's instinct is surely to say that this can't possibly be the case, yet there seems to be considerable disagreement on the issue. Few believe that memes are actually incorporated into our genetic material, but many others think they can have an epigenetic effect on what's then passed on.

Some others, including the great biologist, EO Wilson, believe genes, and the way memes contribute to our culture, work together to influence our development. Wilson, in particular, was to argue in *Genes, Mind and Culture* that genetic and cultural traits interact to affect the pace at which human evolution occurs.

'First, people may vary because they inherited different genes from their parents. Second, genetically similar individuals may differ because they have lived in different environments. Finally, people may differ because they have acquired different beliefs, values and skills.'
Peter Richerson, *Not By Genes Alone*

As to whether ideas are inherited, scientists are forever trying to find evidence for this one way or the other. The neuroscientist Paul Thompson, for instance, has shown how the distribution of brain matter in the frontal cortex that governs self-control can vary between individuals, and that this feature could therefore be a candidate for memetic transfer.

But does that mean that violent, difficult people will have offspring with a similar outlook? Matt Ridley suggests not and that, if anything, the reverse is usually the case. The Australian population as an example, he says, could be expected to have a high proportion of violent convict genes, yet it's one of the most peaceful on earth. Similarly, German culture has changed completely in one or two generations away from their previous group deference to military power.

On the other hand, a recent research project showed that when mice are taught the way through a maze to a reward, there seems to be a degree of faster learning in their offspring when they're set the same task. Similarly in humans, a sample of six-month-old babies were used as guinea pigs recently when they were shown pictures of various potential dangers. Developmental psychologists then tried to see which of them scared the little things - as measured by their pupil dilation.

They found that snakes and spiders freaked them out the most, while far more obvious dangers like lions and bears did not. The reason for this, the researchers suggested, was that even though we're rarely threatened by them these days, venomous creepy crawlies go back as much as forty million years, while larger dangerous animals are much more recent. Perhaps, they concluded, the embedding process simply takes longer to establish itself in our brains than we imagine. And by deduction, if threats can make it through, then why can't moral judgments and behavioural assumptions get in there too?

What no one seems to disagree on is the observation that certain bedrock beliefs can be passed on epigenetically. Among the most quoted cases of these are the ones that relate to racial discrimination. When a persecuted group or race, for example, suffers horribly at the hands of oppressors, then their children appear to inherit many of the neuroses and suspicions that one would expect to find in the parents.

The children of people victimised under the Nazis, for instance, are often found to be just as mentally affected with stress-induced anxieties as those who were actually threatened by the jackboot. This is in spite of these offspring having lived their entire lives in safe, sunny places like California.

How deep do these memes go? After all the thousands of generations we've been recognisably human, is our hardwiring similar to our ancestors, but with knobs on?

Are we, therefore, predictable in our views? Probably not, seems to be the most usual answer, and certainly simple observation seems to argue the opposite. The recent history of mankind appears to show that memes can change over time - or even disappear. Does this mean that they're therefore less firmly anchored in us than we might have been led to think?

For example, many of the memes that one hears people suggest are incapable of being removed ('... that's just what we humans are like') relate to instincts that supposedly govern issues such as gender differences, racial superiority, skin colour, mistrust of strangers, the need to punish people who disagree with us, violent retribution, the compulsion to have children, the benefits of harsh upbringings, superstitions, and all the other sorts of beliefs that once appeared to describe 'the human condition'... but which are now largely seen as absurd or have, to varying degrees, disappeared from our natures.

Indeed, for many of us these aspects of cultural dogma no longer form part of our belief systems. And yet the profound changes between us and our ancestors have only taken a couple of generations to come through. Surely this is a blink in time when set against the hundreds of thousands of years that it took to establish them? Yes, of course, there are still culture wars being fought on most of these issues, but there are very few societies left in which the accepted view on such offensive nonsense hasn't been largely won.

Perhaps the most extraordinary of all conclusions, as I said earlier, is that the impulse to produce offspring - something that is the sole objective of every other organism on earth - has virtually disappeared in us. Now we make our own choices about whether we want to breed. This has to be an extraordinary step change. And yet, to paraphrase Richard Dawkins once more, not only have humans shown a capacity to 'rebel against the tyranny of the selfish replicators' - our genes - but we've also shown we can throw off the influence of our memes if they no longer suit our moral principles or cultural evolution.

'Our minds have been built by selfish genes, but they have been built to be social, trustworthy and cooperative. Human beings have social instincts. They come into the world equipped with pre-dispositions to learn how to cooperate, to discriminate the trustworthy from the treacherous, to commit themselves to be trustworthy, to earn good reputations, to exchange goods and information, and to divide labour.'
Matt Ridley, *The Origins of Virtue*

One meme above all others however, appears to have remained unchanged - and that is our acceptance of authority, the need for leaders, hierarchical power structures, and the idea of a social contract between the governed and those who govern. The Big Man got into our heads early, and he's stayed in there ever since.

Even today, we still tend to view 'elites' with respect and deference, possibly believing at some primordial level, that they *know* more than we do. We instinctively think they must have access to secrets that the rest of us don't - and therefore that they have some kind of natural right to sit at the top of a pyramid, generally with the rest of us at the bottom. Many of us even seem to *like* the idea that our lives and actions can be directed as if we were chess pieces on a board, and actually appreciate being treated in this way. One often hears, for example, how uncomfortable people can become when the smack of firm government is removed.

Anthropologists wonder if the relationship between leaders and the led doesn't date back to the point at which it must have first dawned on the Big Man that he might not be as productive as he'd like it to appear. In fact, it was quite possible his followers could have arrived at the opposite conclusion because, paradoxically, the more able and competent he was, the less there was for him to do.

Horror of horrors, if he wasn't careful, people might actually begin to think he was being parasitic: taking too much from society, and not giving enough back to earn his keep. The result of this awful realisation, the grimmest of insights for social leaders, was that the Big Man was now incentivised to keep up a stream of authoritative decisions and orders, to surround himself with symbols of power, and to make a lot of noise as he bossed people around. But although he'd have kept his anxiety to himself, it also meant he had to be constantly thinking of other ways of holding onto power.

Big Men, of course, had long since established that their families shouldn't appear to be on the same level as lower members of the tribe. There could be none of that raising a sweat that mere labourers did, nor the sort of vile grunting that manual work produced. This was because these types had discovered that by installing memes in their people that they had an indisputable claim to be top dogs, they needed to justify their position with ridiculous fictions about their origins, and wholly imaginary reasons for their continuing power and privileges.

Language supplied this mythology, and any ruling family with a modicum of self-awareness quickly realised that they now had better ways of cementing their right to be in charge than muscle power had ever provided. There were now other levers they could pull that were even more effective.

First, the Big Man would have worked out that knowledge was power, and by keeping all important decisions to himself, and encouraging the support of a priest or shaman caste, he could put out ways of explaining that natural forces and the gods were responsible when things went wrong. And not him. This sort of blame shifting was critical to preserving his power base and he'd have spent a lot of time using it to lay down his infallible superiority.

Next, he usually needed the right to rule to be divinely awarded, and certainly dynastically continued. It could even, at a push, have originally been based on merit.

Thirdly, he needed to shore up his authority by separating himself from the common man with outward signs such as special clothes, ways of speaking, rich artefacts, grovelling servants, separate quarters, honoured spaces, particular decorations, monumental architecture, bling and anything else that puffed him up. Part of his power then came from decreeing that others couldn't have these things.

But, finally, and most importantly for his enduring acceptance, he had to wield power with terrifying violence, summary justice, complex and arbitrary rules, public retribution and madman-like inconsistency. Only by giving himself the ability to decide on life and death could he keep his foot on the community's throat.

As part of this, the Big Man would have realised early on that if his personal projection of the tribe's culture was to be accepted - and his leadership of it - then only his memes could be the right ones. And that meant that every other colony, tribe or race had to be utterly and completely in the wrong.

'The greatest happiness is to scatter your enemies, to drive him before you, to see his cities reduced to ashes, to rob him of his wealth, to see those who love him shrouded in tears and to gather into your bosom his wives and daughters.' Genghis Khan

Quite quickly the Big Man would have come to the conclusion that waging war with outsiders was the perfect recipe for driving home his omnipotence. Victory meant he was in the right, and that he was supported by whatever gods or myths his people followed.

By pitiless vengeance he found he could reduce his enemies, expand his territory, grab land to be ruled by his family and cronies, kill the enemy's men and keep their women as breeding stock. Best of all, he could then pass on his culture and memes into the heads of the vanquished. In this way, his ideas, customs and laws enshrined their culture too, and therefore more people would buy into the fiction of his right to rule. This was how the Big Man got even Bigger.

'States are far less violent than traditional bands and tribes. Modern Western countries, even in their most war-torn centuries, suffered no more than around a quarter of the average death rate of non-state societies, and less than a tenth of that for the most violent one.'
Stephen Pinker *The Better Angels of Our Nature*

It was certainly a high-risk strategy, but if it came off then there were rewards to be reaped: he'd have more power, do less of the work, and distract his people even more from how parasitic he'd become. When he pulled all this off, no one was ever allowed to say the emperor's clothes might even be mildly diaphanous, never mind invisible.

Is this such a preposterous set of criteria that it's laughable in our enlightened and connected world? Hmm, maybe not so fast. Look no further than the Kims of North Korea. The dynasty is a Confucian cult, quasi god-like and worshipped as such, the people are kept totally in the dark while being constantly told they're living in an earthly paradise, no information about the outside world is ever allowed in, and sitting at the peak of the power hierarchy that runs all this is the ultimate Big Man: fat in a race of skinny people, infallible, swaddled in luxury, grinning amongst his anxiety-ridden cronies, capricious and crazily threatening. His rule is maintained by horrible punishments for minor infractions, often handed out to entire families, barbaric killings and a perpetually insecure population. What is this if it isn't a carbon copy of a hunter-gatherer society of 50,000 years ago?

The opposite is also true. The story goes, for instance, that in 1989 as the trickle of East German people trying to leave for the West suddenly grew into a flood, a harassed government official eventually managed to reach Mikhail Gorbachev on the phone.

Could they machine gun the crowd, he asked? No, replied Gorbachev, doubtless after a pause in which he weighed up the international repercussions. There were to be no killings. That was it. In that second Soviet Communism came to a shuddering halt… barring the shouting, the newspaper articles and a few thousand PhD theses. Why? Because if you're going to have a repressive society, and you can't even repress, then what's the point?

Of all the memes that have come down to us, perhaps our core beliefs in the power hierarchies that run our lives - fiscal, government, celebrity, educational, even family - are the most deep-rooted and yet strangely ambivalent. Yes, we recognise they're essential for the order we like in our lives and, yes again, we recognise they drive our cultural evolution… but, no, we sure don't like being bossed about.

Perhaps the final implication of language though, was to be arguably the most profound. This arose because what communication and discussion between humans now allowed us to do was to weigh up situations, discuss the opportunities and threats, and then to make high-speed choices about how to change things.

By doing this, man discovered the trick that our prokaryote ancestors had developed all those billions of years before called Horizontal Gene Transfer. Just as bacteria can adopt entirely new strategies by changing their chemistry without the need to wait for generations to pass, so rapid information transfers meant this could now happen in us humans too. In our case, though, these were not genetic mutations but memetic ones. As William Burroughs was to describe it, language might be a virus, but it's led to dramatic increases in the speed of change on earth.

Radical lurches were suddenly made possible because we could see that there were better ways of progressing as a species, and that we could use helpful innovations to move forward or to get out of trouble. We didn't have to behave like other animals any more, waiting for a chance mutation to come along that might suit us. No, we could now make our own decisions. We began to believe that if we thought about things deeply enough, we could come up with ways of dealing with problems that confronted us. We could find group solutions and, in short, we could take our future into our own hands.

This was the realisation that turbocharged human development. This was when *H. sapiens* really had a claim to the wise bit, because our analytical abilities allowed us to control how we responded to things and shaped our futures, rather than just being a sitting target as other species were when damaging threats came along. Would we be wiped out by rising water levels? No, we'd invent boats and dams. Were there better ways of working and travelling? Yes, we'd invent the wheel, and a harness for draught animals. Would we become extinct because of famines? No, we'd find ways of changing our diet. Would a madman wipe us all out? No, not always, because we'd rebel.

> **'Once you have speech you don't have to wait for natural selection. If you want more strength, you build a stealth bomber, if you don't like bacteria, you invent penicillin, if you want to communicate faster, you invent the Internet. Once speech evolved, all of human life changed.'**
>
> **Tom Wolfe** *The Kingdom of Speech*

Take, for example, the basic tools that the early people used. As the Stone Age progressed, outsourced solutions like the hand axe had been regarded as such a universal tool that it required no improvement. But now humans began to pool their intelligence by communicating with each other - and our natural ingenuity was unleashed.

The result? Better tools, better materials, better ways of achieving things… and the growth of an underlying meme that said innovation could solve problems. There's an old gag among anthropologists that the Stone Age didn't end because people ran out of stone, and it now became obvious why… because language could lead to things being improved. The collective brain was more inventive than any single person could ever be, and we soon found out that there were more useful materials than stone.

Yuval Harari summed up how memes can bring about sea changes in our development in his great book, *Sapiens*: 'Some observers see cultures as a kind of mental inflection or parasite… In just this fashion, cultural ideas live inside the minds of humans.' Later, he continues the point by saying: 'This approach is sometimes called memetics. It assumes that, just as organic evolution is based on the replication of organic information units called genes, so cultural evolution is based on the replication of cultural information units called memes. Successful cultures are those that excel in reproducing their memes, irrespective of the costs and benefits to their human hosts.'

It is thinking like this that has led social historians to see human development as a process that combines both genes and memes into what they call Dual Inheritance Theory.

But if, as Robert Wright has pointed out: '… the more power is centralised, the less technology there's likely to be', how did we shrug off the grip the Big Man had on our lives? How did we take the next great step forward in our development?

How this poor little thing was about to change our cultural evolution.

CHAPTER SIX

HOW WAS MANKIND EVER GOING TO PROGRESS IF THE BIG MAN WAS ALWAYS SQUASHING ANY NEW IDEAS? IT WAS TIME FOR THE FOURTH REVOLUTION AND, AS USUAL, IT WAS THE LITTLE MAN THAT DISCOVERED IT. THE BREAKTHROUGH WAS TO BE A HUMAN VERSION OF 1+1=3, BUT THIS TIME COOPERATION WAS GOING TO BECOME EFFECTIVE WITH PEOPLE OUTSIDE THE COLONY.

Many anthropologists like to say that *H. sapiens'* fourth revolution was when humans began to cooperate with outsiders - people in other tribes. You'd think this had to have been an impossible gulf to bridge if we were instinctively hostile to strangers, but when we actually began to interact through *trading* - it became obvious just how great the gains could be.

And it was at this point that the world changed forever.

Some academics give the idea a scholarly shrug… but what doesn't seem to be greatly disputed is that when specialised skills started to be exchanged, stone-age man then began to move out of his little clans. And he soon realised just how great the benefits could be from forming wider social networks. It was certainly from about this point that the human race started to expand across larger geographic regions, and to allow itself to be exposed to more and more alien cultures.

Why did it happen? Well, don't laugh, but here's how I'd like to imagine a little bit of theatre could have triggered a wholly new way of living…

The young hunter was having a good day. He'd speared a fat rabbit in the late morning and was about to head back to where the tribe had camped for the night when he saw the fresh footprints of a deer, heading away towards a large wood. The man left the rabbit on a branch to be picked up later, and then followed the erratic trail as it weaved between the trees, the marks occasionally becoming confused as the creature stopped to feed from the forest floor.

The man walked lightly, frequently looking up from his tracking to glance nervously about himself, his senses at full pitch. He was only too aware that the slightest sound could give his position away - and there was good reason to be worried. The hunter knew full well that this wooded belt marked the border between his own tribe's hunting lands and the cliffs that dropped down to where the terrifying Sea People lived on the coastal strip. He kept his eyes to the ground, but allowed himself a slight shudder as he recalled some of the stories he'd heard of their barbaric treatment of strangers.

The hunter crept nervously onwards for another mile or so, each step taking him closer to the sound of breaking surf. Eventually he decided he'd drawn a blank, and was about to turn for home when he suddenly saw a young deer upwind of him, in full profile, and grazing placidly on a patch of open ground.

At this range, the poor thing stood no chance. The sharpened wood of the hunter's spear thudded into its flank and it lifted its head momentarily in surprise before going down without a cry. The young man gave a silent victory jig - its meat would mean his family's supper, lunch and tea for the next few days - and he strolled easily over to remove his lance. But as he lifted the little corpse over his shoulders he suddenly stiffened, now aware that he wasn't alone. He swung round and immediately saw a small boy standing by a bush, staring at him with wide, frightened eyes, his face frozen by the sight of the wicked spear's work.

In an instant the hunter had bounded over, the weapon held high above his head. But then he stopped it in mid-air, his eye caught by the sight of what was around the boy's neck. It was the most beautiful thing he'd ever seen… a necklace of shells that seemed to dance in the sun, taking in its light and then throwing it out again in a blaze of colour.

What a prize this was! How he could imagine what that fat Big Man of his would make of it. He could see him now, parading up and down, stroking the beautiful thing and giving everyone else hell. It was obviously a precious thing, and the hunter knew that he *had* to have it… making a present of it to his Chief would see his family in food for far longer than any deer would ever last.

The child was now gibbering in fright as the spear hovered above him, and the hunter began to relax - the boy was clearly out on his own and would hardly be a threat.

But what was he to do? How was he going to get that necklace off him? He began to think through his options. The simplest thing to do was just kill the boy and take it back as fast as his legs could run. But steady on there, he thought, that was bound to provoke a terrible retribution from the Sea People - perhaps even a prolonged conflict.

The Secrets of Life - Book Two

Would his tribe thank him for that?

Maybe it was easier to grab the strings of beads and let the child live? But if he did that then the boy would tell his family that he'd been robbed, and the current uneasy relationship his clan had with them would end. They'd soon be viewing his people as thieves, and any trace of peace or trust would be broken.

Rather more importantly… how would he ever get any more of these gorgeous things if he took either of these approaches?

Leaning forward, he pointed at the beads, grunting at the boy to take them off. But the child didn't move. Hadn't he understood what the hunter meant? Perhaps they were sacred, powerful things, given by the gods? Maybe the child wasn't able to give them up - yes, that would make sense, they looked as if they'd come from the spirits.

Stalemate.

Then, I like to imagine, the young hunter took the step that changed us humans forever. He stabbed his finger at the glowing shells again - and lowered the dead deer from his shoulders and held it up. The child grinned, his terror dissolving. And he stretched his head forward and slipped the necklace over it.

'Every man thus lives by exchanging…'
Adam Smith, *The Wealth of Nations*

The two of them stood for a moment, sizing each other up, and then the hunter twisted his wrist in a circle and pointed at the sun, and then at the ground. Yes, the boy nodded, he would come again this time tomorrow. Hunting animals wasn't a skill of the fish-eating Sea People and the exchange of a deer for such a pathetic row of shells was too good to be turned down. What a fool this man had to be, coming up with such a crazy exchange. It was true that he had a good throwing arm, but if he knew how easy it was to pick these shells up by the water's edge he'd never have offered so much. Of course he'd meet him again… just as long as he could keep him interested in things like this.

Ha. A silly story?

Maybe, but it had to be something like this that led humans to stumble on the fourth revolution to create our culture: the win/win advantages of trading with each other. Anthropologists often talk about how cultural breakthroughs like this can suddenly arise as 'productive mistakes', in that they come out of nowhere. But they act on us in exactly the same way as genetic mutations do.

Incidents like this might not have been planned, but when they happened, people would have been immediately struck by the benefits that could come from exchanging things. In fact, so enormous would they have been that the benefits that arose from the process made it worth running the risk of dealing with potentially dangerous strangers.

Whatever the truth, something along these lines must have occurred to get things going. Why do researchers think that? It's because for some time now, archaeologists have been unearthing ancient shells of the *Nassarius* mollusc in regions that are over a hundred miles inland from the coastlines of North African countries.

It's not unknown for these to be carbon dated to over 100,000 years old, and some even have visible traces of ochre pigment still on them, suggesting they'd been worn as power trophies by the Big Man (or his moll). The shells have usually been selected for their matching sizes, and most significantly they all have holes bored in them that show how they'd have been strung together with a thong.

To make these finds so far from the sea, says the British archaeologist, Bernard Wood: '… suggests that they have cultural value. You wouldn't trudge 200 kilometres if you could find something a lot more local.' No hunter-gatherer tribe, either then or since, has been known to cover an area bordered by these kinds of distances, and this fact alone makes it extremely likely that the shells had been passed from hand to hand. Many of the early axe makers, for example, recognised the risks of crossing another tribe's land and only ever used materials they could find within an hour's walk of their base.

'Our urge to trade has profoundly affected the trajectory of the human species.'
William Bernstein, *A Splendid Exchange, How Trade Shaped the World*

Anthropologists get particularly excited when they find evidence of personal ornamentation like this. They're powerful signs that stone-age men could think symbolically, and that even at this incredibly early date, they're pretty sure that the shells illustrate the deep memetic connection we continue to hold between decoration, cognition, culture and authority.

But if the shells were being traded inland by one group of people to another, then what was coming back the other way? Food and useful animal products probably, but there'd be no trace of these left.

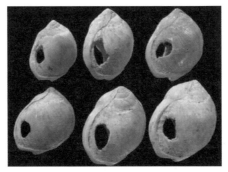

'Shells...

or obsidian? which would
you rather have?'

However, field archaeologists have also found what's known as 'rich man's flint', obsidian, that's plainly made its way in the opposite direction. This rare stone must have been following established trading routes towards the coast, and the conclusion they've come to is that it was being valued by tribes whose hunting areas were a long way from where it originated.

Obsidian is a hard, glass-like substance, formed when lava flows into fresh water, and it was very highly prized by early man for the way it fragments into the sharpest and hardest of cutting edges. This made it, as the geographer, Sarah Brooks says: '… the material of choice for stone knives, arrow points and other tools throughout the prehistoric world.'

But the only obsidian quarries that geologists know of must have been created by the volcanic eruptions that took place in the Ethiopian Rift Valley… and these are as much as 4,000 kilometres away from where the molluscs would have been picked up on the southern shores of the Mediterranean. Clearly, there'd been many pairs of hands passing on these sorts of things in either direction.

Were these the first flickerings of trade? And, if so, how did they shape our future?

Although the benefits of these kinds of exchanges seem so obvious to us now, it was highly unlikely that any Big Man would have sanctioned them if they'd involved contact with people outside his community. The last thing he'd have wanted was another tribe's ideas diluting his community's cultural memes (many of which his ancestors would have invented) let alone questioning the basis of his authority. No, instead of that, it's far more likely that the first trading experiments would have been furtive, secretive affairs that came up from below as the lower social layers tried to find small ways of improving their lives.

But once the mechanism of exchange had been exposed, its astonishing advantages would have made it almost impossible to suppress. The notion that you could get something you wanted from another person by exchanging it for something you didn't particularly value had a hugely compelling logic. The subsistence living and narrow cultures of hunter-gatherer tribes would have made this particularly alluring for them. Simply surviving in those days was a continuous struggle, and anything that made their lives easier must have been enormously attractive.

The cooperation process necessary for trading, of course, wasn't an entirely new meme. These early people had already discovered that they were better off when they divided their labour. But this had only happened *within the colony*. Tens of thousands of years of evolution had led humans to split up their tasks by having men provide the protein from hunted meat, and women forage for stable carbohydrates from the nuts, fruits and vegetables they'd find around them. The end result might have been a gain for the tribe, but activities like this were only ever within their little group.

This exchange of labour between the sexes had plainly evolved to be so deeply held in clan customs that it formed the basis of the mate signalling intimacies of primitive humans. Above all, it had led to the idea of pair bonding between individuals, and this had by now settled down to become a universally accepted social practice.

It remains so, even to this day, and hunter-gatherer tribes are found to be surprisingly stable and equitable societies in which there's virtually no sexism. The sharing out process of men and women trading their different skills has very evidently been passed on as memes to their offspring.

But with the invention of trade, stone-age colonies suddenly found they could get the same kinds of benefits with people they *didn't know*, and who weren't subject to the same cultural rules that were being enforced by their Big Man. No doubt individuals had to be careful about how they went about their meetings and bargains because, from their Chief's point of view, it's hard to see how he'd have allowed this sort of consorting with the enemy to become rooted. If there was cooperation and reciprocity going on - rather than the usual hostility and warfare he was always trying to drum up - then his status at the top of the social pile was bound to come under threat.

Perhaps he simply turned a blind eye to it? Maybe the lure of things like shell bling were just too great a temptation for even old Bossy Boots to resist? Did he think he could control what was clearly a bottom-up process, maybe even to profit from it, if it was obvious that *it didn't need anyone to be in charge?*

However, if the origins of inter-colony trading really were caused by something as hilariously trivial as power dressing, then the consequences of what came after these early exchanges proved to be deeply serious. And they've played a major role in shaping the human species into what we've become today.

Trading would have been a huge step for these early people. They must have been living anxious and insecure lives in worlds that were overflowing with myths, portents and signs. Their leaders ruled largely by fear, and every Big Man would have knocked into his people the meme that neighbouring tribes spelt trouble.

And yet, in spite of all this, his followers had the uncanny ability to project their primitive imaginations towards the idea that they could turn alien people into *customers*. Instead of killing them, they were now worth sparing, because if you did, you could unload your stuff onto them - and also get good things back in return.

On the other hand, it was only worth doing this if you'd let them have something that you didn't particularly value. And this, of course, begged the question of what it was that you could produce that another tribe would definitely want. The logic behind this thought process was critical, because what made this kind of bartering so compelling - and why it was to become universally adopted - was exactly the same then as it is today. What's that? It is because, if a trade is conducted properly, the beauty of it is that *both sides can win.*

Each person wants what the other one has. Yet each of them is putting themselves into the other person's mind, and trying to make it appear that *he's* the one that's winning.

'Each party attaches a higher value to the good he receives than that he gives away.
The exchange ratio, the price, is not the product of equality of valuation, but on
the contrary, the product of a discrepancy in valuation… The card player wins by

Take the example of our little drama. Both the boy with the shells and the hunter with his deer probably each thought that the other one was a complete mug for agreeing to the deal - but both of them would have kept that thought to themselves. Neither would have placed as much value on what they were handing over as they did on what they were getting in exchange... but they weren't going to say that.

Why was that? Well it was because nobody would ever choose to continue trading with someone if he thought he was coming out of it worse off than the other man. Who'd ever want to be a loser? You've got to know you've won... but you've also got to make the other man think that he's won. Matt Ridley gives a vivid example of this in *The Rational Optimist* when he describes how the Indians in the Canadian wilds couldn't believe their luck when the early trappers gave them sharp knives in exchange for a few animal furs. What idiots they thought they were. But you can imagine what the traders thought.

But if trading was a revolutionary breakthrough for humans - how come it had already been established in the natural world? As always, we like to think our huge intellects and personal instincts set us apart from the mindless conflicts that typify non-human behaviour... but is that actually true?

Or were we closer to the behaviour of other organisms when we 'invented' trading than we could ever possibly have imagined?

**Two little boys about to chop through
the mysteries of relationships.**

CHAPTER SEVEN

IS TRADING BETWEEN HUMANS SO VERY DIFFERENT FROM THE SPECIALISATION AND EXCHANGE OF ASSETS THAT ONE SEES IN THE NATURAL WORLD? NON-HUMAN 'TRADING' OCCURS AS SYMBIOTIC RELATIONSHIPS, AND THEY CLEARLY EVOLVED TO SUIT BOTH PARTIES. BUT DID WE INVENT AN ENTIRELY NEW VERSION OF THIS WHEN WE DID THE SAME SORT OF THING?

The long history of evolution I've had a go at outlining in these books has consistently shown that organisms can benefit from finding profitable ways of coexisting with the other things around them. Sometimes this might mean simply surviving without getting into trouble, but frequently life forms found that they could come to symbiotic arrangements that would lead to mutual advantages.

The different ways in which this happens show how cooperation has run like a thread through the entire history of life. In fact, it's nothing but the 1+1=3 process that's been creating gains for things from the first bacterial cells onwards. And it was this same life force that ultimately made it possible for sophisticated creatures like ourselves to function and prosper. It was how organisms came to live together, and how they then evolved ecological arrangements that suited them. And it was what drove, and continues to drive, the 'life decisions' that shape how everything developed its behavioural strategies.

The way things act to achieve these outcomes eventually saw them taking up varying positions on the Behavioural Spectrum I described in the last book. At one extreme of this scale is the 'grab everything' tactic of parasitoids. This choice had the disadvantage of killing the host, however, and other organisms adopted strategies in which both parties continued to live, and then shared in the benefits of symbiotic relationships to a greater or lesser extent.

At the other end of the Spectrum it was possible to see how this strategy was taken to the extreme, when they somehow evolved new versions of the altruistic, self-sacrificing tactics of single-celled organisms. This was at its most evident among the intricate arrangements of eusocial insects.

But to repeat one of the major themes of evolutionary theory that lies behind these choices: when everything's boiled down, what propels this decision-making process is the compulsion of every single living thing to prosper in one of two fundamental ways. In the first group, organisms are trying to beat other things - perhaps eating them or somehow making them their slaves.

This approach is described as 'zero sum' in that they're attempting to win by making something else lose. In other words, the process has a zero increase in *efficiency* because one party's energy is simply being transferred to the other. This is like the heat transfer process of the 1st Law of Thermodynamics - but now apparent in biology rather than in physics.

The second group employs the alternative approach. This is when organisms choose to live cooperatively with the other life forms around them, and here they attempt to win by allowing their partners to win too. In doing this they're aiming to create a *gain* between them, because their joint efforts are making life's processes more efficient.

It's the prospect of achieving this that leads evolutionary biologists and social scientists to say that when there's cooperation between different energy-consuming forms, then life is countering the 2nd Law. And instead of being zero sum, they term the joint benefits of these associations as 'non-zero'.

To the human mind, with our deeply embedded memes about fairness and moral behaviour, this division in strategies probably looks like they're definitions of selfishness and unselfishness. But this is a misleading interpretation because the long story of evolution has shown that any examination of the 'selfish' gene at work - from the way it encourages death, right through to the reasons it makes organisms behave sacrificially - all highlight that these definitions bear no resemblance to our human descriptions. Instead, what's being played out is simply a breathtakingly clever series of survival strategies.

Nothing is ever being wholly selfish if it manages to keep *life* going. Nor is it necessarily being 'nice' if it behaves synergistically - whether by commensalism, mutualism or altruism. Cooperation is simply winning in another way to being openly competitive. One shouldn't be lulled into thinking that selflessness is in any sense charitable if it helps colonies and communities do better. Sadly that isn't the case. Rather, it stems from another form of genetic selfishness… but admittedly one that appears to have rather nicer table manners and a more elegant set of clothes.

Humans are no different to other living things in making this profound strategic choice. We, too, can be either selfish or selfless in our behaviour. But where our evolutionary path has made us unique among multicellular organisms is that we've perfected the fantastic trick of *not having to limit ourselves to just one position on the Behavioural Spectrum*.

How have we managed that? Well, everything besides us has evolved in such a way that at some stage they've all made a genetic 'decision' about their choice of survival strategy. They arrived at a way of behaving with the other life forms around them - and then stuck with it until sudden change turned it into a failure.

We don't make that permanent choice. We, alone, can move smoothly around, changing where we stand in an instant, sometimes being selfish and sometimes the opposite. We use our instincts and reasoning abilities to decide on our actions depending on how we weigh up the environmental situation, or how others may be behaving, or how we think we might 'win'. Even though this process is completely instinctive and operates in a blink, we're nonetheless constantly deciding on what we're going to say and do.

Every decision we arrive at depends on what we think would suit us best - either at that moment or at some point in the future. It may not look like it, but what we're trying to achieve by doing this is to get an advantage over other people by 'dealing' with them. Yet in doing this we've now moved far beyond the crude mechanism of barter, and have ended up with a wider and infinitely more sophisticated process.

Now we trade at all times, and in pretty much every aspect of our lives, doing this not just with our assets and abilities, but in how we communicate our thoughts and views, our emotions and attributes, and in how we apply our skills, produce and values.

**'A good marriage, like any partnership, means subordinating one's own
needs to that of the other's, in the expectation that they will do the same.'
Nicholas Sparks, *True Believer***

These multifaceted abilities allow us to slide around in our behaviour - sometimes grabbing an advantage over other people and sometimes sharing the benefits of cooperation with them. And our capacity to perfect the process shot forward in increasingly sophisticated ways once we'd grown our huge brains and added the power of language. We moved on from exchanging things through dividing our labour, or making clumsy swaps of things like shells and deer. Over time we refined our capabilities until we ended up with the hugely complicated and sophisticated reciprocal arrangements that every one of us now takes for granted.

> '... human beings display a behavioural scale, a spectrum of responses
> that appear or disappear according to particular circumstances.'
> EO Wilson, *On Human Nature*

We may not even be aware we're doing it. Yet we're constantly, instantly and brilliantly weighing up what we want, and then transacting with others around us. We're doing this because we've each developed a colossal basket of specialisations, attitudes, opinions, relationships, responsibilities, beliefs, memes and everything else that make up our lives. And it's the extraordinary capacity we have to operate like this within our social networks that have combined to make us such an advanced species.

This was how we developed beyond just using genetic evolution to make our life 'decisions', and came to employ the benefits of our cultural evolution as well. Unlike other things, we didn't just choose from a narrow range of symbiotic relationships. Instead, we turned ourselves into a protean master race, uniquely able to keep shifting our behaviour depending on how we're trying to succeed.

This ability may have resulted in us becoming the most advanced of organisms, but it's also made us have maddeningly elusive personalities. Just as other species are making their genetic decisions at the same time as the other things around them that are also evolving, *so we're continually adapting and adjusting ourselves in a world in which others are doing the same thing.*

What everyone's learnt from this is how to move around in an apparently effortless and unconscious way, sometimes acting truthfully and sometimes being deliberately misleading; sometimes sincere, sometimes bluffing; sometimes being engagingly transparent and sometimes dissembling; sometimes being loyal, and sometimes swapping sides. At all times, however, we're shifting around depending on how we think we might come out on top.

We never rest. In fact, we've even come to say that we're 'dealing with people' to describe how we coexist. Dealing - making deals - is such second nature to us that we probably never stop to think about it, nor do we regard these exchanges as 'trades'. Rather, we've perfected the process to the point where our strategies are so instinctive in us that they can only be described as *innate*.

Every now and then, though, one sees or hears something that brings home what's going on. I had an example of this the other day when I found myself listening to a heated spat between two brothers, one aged about five and the other around seven, who were fighting over which of them should have which plastic chainsaw. I'd made the mistake of buying them the two different toys, and their view was that they weren't each as good as the other. Now one of the little chaps wanted what his brother had… but how to get him to give it up?

The way they marshalled their arguments, brought up old debts and favours as balancing items from previous bargains, tried pleading at some points and using aggression at others, added the menace of appealing to their mother for justice, sweetened the deal with other possessions and favours, threatened violence, passionately explained to one another why he was, in fact, the one that was gaining when he thought he wasn't, and kept changing their lines of attack as they tried to manoeuvre each other around.

I listened transfixed. Mr Chomsky may have given up on the idea of us having a language organ in the brain, but listening to those two dealing with each other with all the assurance of merchant bankers negotiating a complicated corporate acquisition made me realise how our trading skills must have entered so deeply into our psyches that they've become a wholly natural part of our existence.

What was interesting about the drama was how quickly it was over. Within five minutes of having the wildest of rows, the entire incident had disappeared into the ether. The boys had moved on to other things, and the toys were completely forgotten.

The only conclusion I could come to was that they'd been acting out the same kind of ritualised conflict routine that John Maynard Smith thought organisms like his stags followed. The actual cause of the boys' quarrel might not really have mattered, but each was passionately arguing to show the other his boundaries and trading strengths. What they were displaying were their personalities, and in the process they were learning through play, perfecting their bargaining techniques, and honing the key skills of life on each other.

This is how the world works. Just as every organism is making its evolutionary decisions at the same time that everything else is doing the same thing, so we, too, are operating in a constantly shifting landscape in which everyone around us is equally pursuing their own aims.

Everywhere we look there are people defending their interests, feeding their egos and calming their psychological drives: sometimes they're being truthful, occasionally they're lying, but above all, whether we like to face up to it or not, they're trying to win.

The blizzard of stimuli we receive from other people are collectively what's giving us our endless challenges - and yet our constant opportunities. Being able to cope with this barrage is how we survive in the world. Now one can see this, it's less surprising that social scientists and anthropologists conclude that it's these constant mental dealing processes that most define us as a *sentient* species.

But are the outcomes of our decisions conforming to some kind of deep directional force - like the ocean currents of evolutionary forces that the fictional Guru referred to in his analogy? Well, to probe a little deeper - and don't curl your lip at the story - but try and answer what appears to be the silliest of questions about our two chainsaw rivals. It's a scenario that may appear to be an unrealistic drama yet, astonishingly, it's one of the core building blocks that evolutionary theorists use to explain the way that humans have developed.

Think again about the two feisty, argumentative little boys and their dispute. The only certainty was that they were unable to agree on anything without a squabble. Now put in front of them another source of potential disagreement. It's the most delicious cake they've ever seen, oozing with cream and awash with chocolate sauce. Got the picture? But here's the problem… you're the person holding the knife, and you've got to somehow find a way of dividing it fairly between the two of them.

So, how are you ever going to slice it into exactly equal halves?

What's going to happen? Trouble of course… because when you offer one of them the choice about which 'half' he wants, whatever he picks is bound to provoke howls of rage from the other that has the 'smaller' piece. Knowing their personalities and infant paranoia, whoever hasn't had a choice in the matter is bound to think that he's been treated unfairly.

So here's the question… how do you divide the cake to be certain both boys will accept what they end up with? How can peace break out? Get this right, say the theorists, and we're on our way to understanding how everything in life makes its decisions. The answer is given in the next book - and explaining its importance is something that I hope to unfold as the arguments continue.

First, though, go back to the steps involved in human trading. The original tentative experiments may have just been crude bartering… but are we still using the same mechanisms today that we arrived at all those tens of thousands of years

The Secrets of Life - Book Two

ago? And are we still making our lightning decisions in a similar way to how those primitive men were?

Yup, we are, just the same. In fact, not only are we doing this, but we're also using the same processes for exchanging our specialisations that the natural world employs in its symbiotic arrangements. The difference is that we make our exchanges in a nanosecond, and other organisms take the generations needed for genetic mutations. And the untold stages of trial and error that this will involve.

'Be nice! Just pick a piece.
They look exactly the same.'

Where the procedural steps are completely similar, though, is that every cooperative, exchange-based relationship has to do more than just suit one party. For them to repeatedly work, there have to be gains for the other side as well. Just like us when we make our deals, logic dictates that no living thing would ever continue to trade if it knew it was going to be the losing party. There *has* to be an incentive for both of them, or you can kiss goodbye to any chance of finding a collaborative relationship.

Hold on, though, you're probably saying. Most humans throughout our history have been bullied, suppressed and threatened by Big Men and their enforcers... so where were the symbiotic gains in all those relationships?

Well, three answers I think. First, for large numbers of humans, simply being led and not having to ponder too deeply about thir own lives is a gain. Quite a lot of us like having tight guidelines to live by, and still do.

Secondly, in authoritarian societies, we might not have liked them, but staying on the right side of the ruler's laws was what kept one alive. It wasn't always bad, either, because many of us think there are real benefits to be had from being on the winning side, particularly if the Big Man's fictions and myths created a triumphalist culture. No doubt Napoleon had spotted this quirk when he famously said that: 'The human race is governed by its imagination.'

And, thirdly, being on the wrong side of these relationships was hardly much of an incentive to be cooperative, let alone to go the extra mile. It's for this reason that the world's come to realise that any government system that's based on a lack of concern for its subjects is ultimately counter-productive. Things like slavery, repression, tyranny, exploitation and all the other 'let them eat cake' approaches inevitably lead to everything going down the plughole. North Korea or Singapore, anyone? Take your pick.

> '**I was not born to be forced. I will breathe after my**
> **own fashion. Let us see who is the strongest.'**
> **Henry David Thoreau, *On the Duty of Civil Disobedience***

No doubt you're asking why we need or want to have these transactional lives anyway. Aren't there simpler ways of living?

Well, the answer to this goes right back to the description I tried to give in the last book about the beginning of the Universe. That was when, in the mind-boggling split second of the Big Bang, the laws that govern how energy can neither be created nor destroyed, but also how every interaction will lead to entropy, were forged as the cornerstones of existence. These forces shaped every evolutionary transition there's ever been and, ultimately, made all organisms, including us, try to avoid having to do everything for ourselves.

Deep within each and every life form, even within its very biochemistry, there's always been the underlying drive to join up with other things so that tasks can be shared out. If they can do that, then *it's possible there are energy savings*. Life becomes more efficient and, in their own tiny way, these relationships reduce the forces of entropy. Cooperation, in other words, leads to energy efficiencies - and energy is what keeps life going.

Humans may like to think we're the bee's knees as a species, but when we cooperate through trading we're really doing no more than chemical compounds did when elements first joined up to create them, or cyanobacteria does in plant life, or any other symbiotic arrangement carries out in the natural world.

And that's because, like them, we're all geniuses at creating synergies. In short, it's the very opposite of the effort that's lost in zero sum relationships. Edward Bellamy summed this up in his great Utopian novel, *Looking Backward* when he wrote: 'Competition, which is the instinct for selfishness, is another word for dissipation of energy, while combination is the secret of efficient production.'

In this sense, our human behaviour is no different to anything else in the natural world. Just as in Nature, though, virtually no symbiosis is ever wholly balanced or truly mutualistic in the share-out of its benefits.

Where we humans differ from other living things, though, is that instead of just having a small number of these arrangements, we live in a cloud of them, constantly relying on the people around us - and having them equally dependent on us. This is what makes us so alert to what we're getting out of our relationships. And it's what leads us to ditch some as we go along, and to create new ones, as well as carefully maintaining those that we most need.

As ever, it's extremely rare that both parties could ever be defined as making equal gains. One is always, almost by definition, going to be getting more out of an exchange than the other.

Nonetheless, this doesn't stop us and other things from entering into these arrangements. Ultimately, they all prove to be beneficial, and putting up with any tensions that might arise is just the price to be paid for the advantages. HG Wells was to describe how hostile symbioses can become when he concluded that: '... even in human affairs, partnerships for mutual benefit are not so easily kept up.'

Even our bodies are examples of the principle. Our cells are eukaryotic, formed by the combination of two earlier life forms, and yet these building blocks are themselves the result of an uneasy cooperation. John Maynard Smith described this when he referred to the mitochondria within them as being like 'slaves'. One might almost say that these hard-working parts of the cell 'may not like the arrangement' and might even be regarded as 'doing more work than the nucleus'... but that doesn't mean that either party would actually want a divorce.

In exactly the same way, we put up with the inequalities and unfairnesses that are bound to crop up in our exchanges. Instead of continuously demanding that they're rebalanced, most of us show a remarkable flexibility and tolerance in the way we wait for a rebalancing to take place. But this doesn't mean that each of us isn't keeping a kind of ledger in our heads, setting down in it which actions and debts will need to be sorted out at some point if our future exchanges aren't going to irretrievably break down.

This mythical accounts book of ours explains why we're instinctively capable of weighing up unequal symbiotic relationships, and yet are still capable of coming to the conclusion that they can suit us. Sometimes we'll even set the calculation to one side and accept that if we're getting something we want, then we're not going to dwell too long on what the other side might be gaining.

Nevertheless, we're acutely alive to the possibility of being exploited. And we all know the feeling we get when we think the split of benefits is too unbalanced, or that we're being taken for granted. A reaction of some kind inevitably follows.

Where our forbearance shows the greatest flexibility, however, is within families and in dealing with close relations. Repeated research studies into this suggest that when we're being so patient with people we share genes with, we're echoing the kin selection mechanism that operates so profitably in Nature. When we're related, it seems, we tend to be more forgiving.

But while cooperative relationships may have built societies, the question of *perceived* value is still one that plagues every exchange and every bargain - and makes them so tricky. The deer and shells swap, for instance, must have been heaven for both parties when it was first dreamt up, but if it had been repeatedly offered, how long would it have been before one of the parties got fed up? What if one side decided it had enough shells, or the other one simply couldn't endlessly supply meat? What if one of them upped the price?

The problem with the barter method of those early deals was that it was too unsubtle an approach. Besides anything else, it depended on both sides wanting what the other had - at the same time. There was no concept of delayed reciprocity. Yet unlike the symbioses seen in the natural world, stone-age men now had the intelligence to *imagine* what the counterparty was thinking, and even to work through how they might be replaced as a deal partner by someone else. Or put under pressure to change their terms.

Because of this danger, even prehistoric people would have realised pretty quickly that they'd have had to find some kind of balancing mechanism that they could use to smooth out any perceived difference in benefits.

> **'When only one party makes a profit that's**
> **robbery, when all parties make a profit, that's business.'**
> **Amit Kalantri, *Wealth of Words***

Of course, we now use money to do this. It's added to one side or the other in a bargain. Or it acts on its own as a way of transferring stored value into the future. And the beauty of it as a virtual mechanism is that everyone signs up to its value.

However, the ancient traders didn't have such a thing to even out their inequalities. Without it, they'd have found that the only way to project their exchanges into future settlements was with huge dollops of trust that any injustice would be sorted out at a later date. We understand that now... but it's a tough concept to grasp when you don't even have a common language to explain what you're trying to do.

This lack of an *outsourced basis of trust* would have created enormous barriers to allowing barter to progress towards true commerce. It's therefore unsurprising to learn that anthropologists have identified a huge gap in the evidence of exchanges taking place between the first 'shells and obsidian' trading routes of 100,000 years ago, and the later evidence of buying and selling networks that took off once tribes had spread throughout Europe around 30,000 years ago.

The difference between the two time periods, of course, was that by then sophisticated *languages* would have developed. This was when merchants began to arrive who'd have oiled the wheels of communication between the various tribes and communities. They'd also have handled the transport issues, and all this external smoothing unquestionably led to people achieving increasingly complicated trades.

> **'Trade may seem a very pragmatic activity, one that needs no fictive basis. Yet**
> **the fact is that no animal other than *Sapiens* indulges in trade, and all the *Sapiens'***
> **trade networks about which we have detailed evidence were based on fictions.**
> **Trade cannot exist without trust, and it's very difficult to trust strangers.'**
> **Yuval Noah Harari, *Sapiens***

Slowly, from around this time, memes were being established about the benefits that could flow from exchange and barter. Entire cultures were beginning to rely on getting things they needed from the outside, rather than from within their colonies. Humans may have been hunter-gatherers for something like 90% of the time we've been on earth, but once our ancestors worked out how trading exchanges could help them - in spite of the Big Man's opposition - then our behavioural patterns completely shifted.

Did all of us see things in the same way? No, of course not, and many people still don't. For these types, relationships are still viewed through a zero sum lens in which other people are considered to be fair game, mugs to be taken for a ride. Most of us, however, have evolved to reject this approach, and instead regard the advantages that come from trading as self-evident.

> **'Teamwork is not a game for the selfish. It is for those**
> **with the mindset that a win for one is a win for all.'**
> **Michael Bassey Johnson, *The Angel of Compassion***

This general realisation brought with it a profound influence on the evolutionary direction of humans. Since our stone-age ancestors had first blundered around with their crude bargains, the gains that were possible from trading were to bring fundamental changes to the way we viewed other people… and most of them were for the better.

Really? Better?

What were they?

'What's this I hear about your trading idea.'

CHAPTER EIGHT

MOST PEOPLE WOULD AGREE THAT GETTING THINGS YOU WANTED BY DEALING WITH COOPERATIVE PEOPLE HAD TO MAKE LIFE EASIER - BUT WHY HAS THIS SKILL BECOME SO IMPORTANT TO US? WHY IS THE DEVELOPMENT OF SPECIALISATION AND EXCHANGE NOW RECKONED TO HAVE BEEN ONE OF MANKIND'S KEY REVOLUTIONS?

Just as walking led to running, and from there to our powers of endurance and persistence; or just as fire led to cooking, and from there to brain growth, language and the development of our imaginations… so the discovery of the efficiencies we can make from 'trading' relationships were now profoundly shaping the way we viewed other people.

As time passed, we increasingly found that seeing others as potential cooperators, rather than perilous enemies, could bring real benefits. And when this realisation sank in, profound memes began to cascade down that progressively shaped our neuropsychology, and so drove our behaviour.

The first of these came as the penny dropped about how beneficial the process of specialisation and exchange could be. The consequence of us using the process, however, was the realisation that to get what you wanted from someone, you had to have something that you could sell or exchange in return. This may seem obvious to us now with our jobs and other ways of making money, but it would have been a revolutionary idea to people who simply lived off the land.

Nonetheless, however primitive a people might be, they could still see that the reason that things like deer could be swapped for assets like shells, was because neither of the parties had what the other one did. If these exchange relationships were to work, therefore, then it wasn't so much what the other person possessed that mattered - it was what *you* had. If what you owned was desirable to another person - then so were you.

But when we're dealing with people, we don't just make ourselves attractive by carting around dead deer or a string of beads. So where else can a person's worth come from? Well, nowadays we live in a hugely interconnected world in which values arise from a wide range of sources: from our skills and functions, our qualities and personalities, even from our reputations. And, the greater the attractions a person has, the more there is to trade. Lionel Messi, for instance, might not be of great use as a gardener, but he's so sublime at football that this makes him able to exchange that one skill for an enormous range of other things.

The second meme that now became so ingrained in us that it shaped our very development, was the recognition that if we wanted people to deal with us, then we had to stop thinking about *our* requirements and desires… and to think instead about *what they want, and what they need*. Why them? Because the only sure way to keep people buying from you is to make certain that they keep winning from the deal. If we don't, and they get a better offer from someone else - whether it's a dead deer, a hire car, doctor, hair shampoo, affection or any other product, service or emotional reward - then they'll drop you and start exchanging with them instead.

This monitoring process of *other* people's requirements is now completely instinctive in us - but ignore it and one can suffer the consequences. Companies can lose market share just as easily as children can lose their friends. And our hunter-gatherer ancestors would have quickly worked this out as well, because the mechanics of early exchanges were really no different to the demands that shape any other transaction. And what they would soon have realised was that these arrangements could actually be formalised.

How's that possible?

Well, start with the most obvious consequence: if one side cheats the other, what does the loser do? He'll then avoid the bad guy, and any trust there might have been will be lost. Not only that, but the word gets around that the person isn't trustworthy, and his reputation would be trashed. This is potentially disastrous for him, because while it's always been the case that you can sell something once… if you let people down, then you won't sell it a second time.

The upshot of this is that if you want a continuous trading relationship - then you have to treat the other person with respect. If the counterparty thinks you're getting more out of the arrangement than they are, then they'll either stop dealing with you or they'll find someone else who'll give them a better offer. This all means that it's only by having a constant *concern* for others that we can keep up our relationships with them.

What an extraordinary conclusion this must have been for early man to have arrived at… to have moved from seeing outsiders as enemies, to having to care for them because they wanted to continue to trade was immense. What a major cultural force must have been unleashed when this kind of realisation first entered their heads.

But not everyone saw things that way. Trading with outsiders was always disliked by Big Men because they found it hard to control, and would have regarded it as a threat to their authority. Their instinct was always to see strangers as people to be feared, or exploited at best, and they spent much of their time establishing memes in the minds of their clan that the subjugation and slavery of others was preferable to exchanging things with them.

Hammering people who weren't in your tribe into submission meant having more people to boss about, more people who'd see you as the rightful leader and more subjugated people to do the menial work.

This was how the world worked for millennia and, to some extent, it continues to this day. Nevertheless it defied logic. Slaves or even a mass of valueless peasants were highly unlikely to ever become customers, and this meant that they could only occasionally be incentivised or motivated by anything other than fear. They wouldn't become consumers, they couldn't grow the economy, they'd never be fully trusted, and they'd always be wildly unproductive.

Without the competitive edge that comes from trading, they'd also very rarely come up with any useful innovations.

> 'Slavery weakens a worker's incentive to work… (it) keeps them from becoming robust consumers…(and) by keeping labour artificially cheap, slavery dampens the society's incentive to develop more productive technologies.'
> Robert Wright, *Nonzero*

In short, subjugation was a moronic system. But when did this logic ever stop it? Instead, it was how the majority lived for tens of thousands of years. So why did it persist? Arguably, it stemmed from the fear Big Men have always had for being seen as the parasitic drag on progress that they so plainly are. Their instinctive response to overcoming any threat this might provoke has always been to distract their people by becoming a remote and terrifying presence.

There were various tricks to achieving this, but the most commonly employed were to avoid being near anyone but their closest circle, to keep repressing the common folk, to endlessly favour retainers, to encourage myths about themselves, and to keep their people off balance with internal presumption and external violence.

'Can't I just be nice and tell the truth?'

Sometimes they even chucked in a few divine powers and distancing techniques to turn their subjects to jelly. No one would be allowed to come near a king, for example, and certainly not to touch them. By the time of the Middle Ages, the 'Royal Touch' was so rare that it had become charged with sacred power, and was sometimes regarded as a miraculous cure for horrible diseases.

Some cultures took this kind of separation to absurd levels. Robert Wright relates in *Nonzero* how Polynesian chiefs wouldn't even permit their people to *look* at them, a blanket instruction that was known as 'tapu' from which we get the word 'taboo'.

> **'It is an iron rule of history that every imagined hierarchy disavows its fictional origins and claims to be natural and inevitable. Any distinctions… are all rooted in fiction. Unfortunately complex human societies seem to require these imagined orders… the upper levels enjoyed privileges and power, while the lower ones suffered from discrimination and oppression.'**
> **Yuval Noah Harari *Sapiens***

Yet absolute power like this proved to be a dangerous game. Punishment and suppression were parts of a ratchet process that didn't allow for later tolerance. Even an occasional slackening of top-down violence was usually rewarded by being overthrown. But at the root of the system lay a great irony, because by ignoring the very people who were allowing them to be parasitical, rulers had to favour their close kin and cronies to keep the delusion going. One slip and they were done for.

And this meant that these Big Men had to be right all the time, or the next lot in the hierarchy would bring them down. It was a rigid, pitiless, zero sum system, and it almost always ended in a destructive implosion.

Set against this, trading and other non-zero activities came up from below - from the lower layers of society - and it was this natural force, rather than Big Men, that drove the gradual evolution of cooperation in humans. Specialisation and exchange depended on establishing lasting relationships and this led to memes that saw mankind moving gradually away from random savagery, on to less awful forms of barbarism, then to mutual concern and, eventually, to civilisation.

A further influence that trading brought to our cultural development was to see us develop our instinctive ability to predict who would be trustworthy and who was likely to be cooperative.

Who was likely to free ride in deals, for example, or even to cheat? Matt Ridley quotes some remarkable research to illustrate just how innate this ability has become in us in *The Rational Optimist*. He reports that people's forecasts of who might be trusted to behave fairly - and who wouldn't be - are accurate around 80% of the time. This assessment process, he believes, can happen even if they'd only had a *glance* at the person they were being asked to sum up. In particular, people were also found to be extremely accurate when asked to remember the faces of those who'd cheated them.

Just as in the natural world, while being abusive might give someone a short-term gain, a longer-term disadvantage was very likely to come with it. Why was that? It's because when offenders are exposed it makes forming relationships far more difficult for them in the future. Their reputations suffer. And if this is part of the process of finding a mate, then genetic selection takes over and, over time, the genes of people with a zero sum or devious outlook become less likely to be passed on. *Bad people will then logically decline in numbers, and cooperation will naturally evolve.*

What does all this add up to? Well, in summary, it results in nothing less than a prescription for caring about relationships and for developing an instinctive awareness of what other people might need or be pleased by. This might appear counterintuitive, but the reasoning is inescapable. Just as Bill Hamilton showed that altruism originated from genetic selfishness, so too does our approach to collaboration. It's easy to portray this as a touchy, feely concept - much scorned by zero summers - but our cultural evolution has shown that it's actually deeply rooted in hard-headed, savvy and self-interested decision making.

But does this mean that evolutionary theorists and social scientists therefore regard 'fair dealing' as simply a *gambit*? And that underneath it all, we humans are just cynical automatons, only concerned about the needs of others - because they'll serve our own selfish ends?

Well, I very much doubt anyone would go quite that far. But, yes, the origins of our collaborative behaviour did arise from our drive for 1+1=3-style gains, yet beneficial social interactions have now settled down in our hardwiring to be deeply and sincerely held.

What may have begun as a logical tactic in primitive man has plainly ended up with us having a moral outlook about the need to consider the welfare of others. The memes that make us behave in this way have morphed into ethical truths, and a concern for our neighbours is now regarded as an admirable human quality. But none of this stops us from taking a step backwards and seeing how these behavioural patterns first emerged.

When we discovered the advantages of trading all those tens of thousands of years ago (although even this is just a tiny proportion of mankind's evolutionary history) it was the resulting need for fairness in relationships that ultimately led to our largely peaceful, cooperative and moral societies.

Yet the paradox at the heart of the story is that the cultural revolution was initially triggered by tentative meetings between people who'd have been *terrified* of each other. Thank goodness we managed to overcome this barrier, one might well say, because the results that flowed from our furtive interactions led to us not wanting to bop the other person on the head... but to keep him alive and productive, and even well disposed towards us.

Over the longer term, the growing exchange of products and specialist skills produced increasingly complicated social networks. And as humans became better at exploiting the advantages of trading, our expertise took us further and further away from our animal origins. The conclusion to the process, as Robert Wright relates in *Nonzero*, was that: '... non-zero behaviour gets replicated because winning cultures are generally based on cooperation... (and that) memes bringing productive harmony get admired and adopted.'

Alongside the concept of exchanging our specialisations with peoples outside our colonies, we developed the idea that each of the parties could expect the other one to behave in the way they said they would. We created, in other words, the conditions for *trust* to exist. And once we'd worked out what this meant, we then moved on to seeing the benefits of fair collaboration, and the insight widened beyond just individual dealing, and eventually brought moral memes into societies as a whole.

The logic for all this was outlined by Marcus Chown in *What A Wonderful World* when he explained that once repeated trading patterns were established, then social improvements were bound to follow: '… since the end of the last Ice Age, it is clear what the driving force of most human innovation has been: Interaction. Interaction. Interaction.'

Of course, by interacting like this, we increasingly linked up with people outside our communities. This led to a virtuous circle. Not only were we making further gains, but instead of us constantly being fearful of how dissimilar we were, we found that other people were actually pretty much the same as us, particularly in our collective desires. Matt Ridley highlights how this discovery remains with us even today when he says in *The Origins of Virtue*: 'That's why, for all their superficial differences of language and custom, foreign cultures are still immediately comprehensible at the deeper levels of motives, emotions and social habits.'

'Without trust, there's no cooperation. And, without cooperation, there's no progress.'
Rick Yancey, *The Last Star*

As trading expanded throughout the prehistoric period, it became increasingly apparent that cooperative groups did better than those in which the Big Man and his cronies continued to forbid contact with outsiders. Natural selection now began to operate at the group level rather than the individual, and our big brains were adding a perception of *value* to measuring out our trades. All this contributed to making transacting societies thrive, while selfish, fearful, internally-directed ones did not.

Gradually this realisation expanded contact even with the most recalcitrant of communities, and with it came an interest in the lives of others and the rewards that could come from investing in getting to know and understand them. Memes developed that recognised the benefits of ethical behaviour, and how these stemmed largely from peaceful fair-dealing, putting trust at the centre of our relationships, and the avoidance of violence.

Ah, violence. This, of course, was pretty much all the Big Man understood. Being good at it was what funded his lust for expansion. Paradoxically though, as I explain more fully later, it also had the effect of expanding trade, because history was to prove that the larger a society became, the greater the opportunities were for specialist skills, and therefore for profitable exchanges.

'Even if we do have inclinations towards violence, we also
have inclinations to empathy, to cooperation and to self-control.'
Steven Pinker, *The Better Angels of Our Nature*

Yet another consequence of the trading revolution began to arise when people were offered the same thing - but by different sources. If an entrepreneurial Sea Person, for example, had put out feelers to other tribes to expand his shells for meat adventures, then what would have happened? Competition would have worked its usual magic… prices would have no doubt dropped, deals might have become enhanced ('exchange one deer and get a second free') or maybe the tribe's cooks would have started to add value with a few sweeteners ('now with a cranberry and apple sauce').

Who knows what juicy titbits these stone-age people would have come up with - but the only certainty was that as ever… *competition would have bred innovation.*

'Innovation is the creation and delivery of new customer value in the marketplace.'
Michael Gelb, *Innovate Like Edison*

Whether the offers were novel, or whether they came from doing something different, or even if they stemmed from sellers being more attentive or flexible didn't really matter - just as long as both parties in a transactional relationship kept their standards high and their offering fresh. Yuval Harari wrote about exactly this consequence in *Sapiens*, when he said that this development would have: '… opened a fast lane of cultural evolution, bypassing the traffic jams of genetic evolution… (and the result was that we)… soon far outstripped all the other human and animal species in our ability to cooperate'.

But even though people were involving themselves in quite complicated trades by 30,000 or so years ago, they were still stuck with the problems of having small societies, and this meant that the opportunities for specialised skills were limited. This was undoubtedly a barrier to expansion, and it was made worse as Big Men were set on keeping strangers away - and instead saw violence against them as a way of enforcing their authority.

Yes, bartering and other exchanges might have made life a little easier… but we were still in one of those evolutionary dead ends. To overcome this, how were we ever going to scale our societies up?

And how would this help us have the scope for more specialist offerings?

'An apple! Is this your idea of giving a girl
a good time... you call this a date?'

SIZEABLE SOCIETIES WERE SOON TO EMERGE WITH MANKIND'S FIFTH REVOLUTION - THE BIRTH OF AGRICULTURE. AND WITH THIS CAME A HUGE EXPANSION IN SKILLS, HIERARCHIES, TRADING, COOPERATION AND SOCIAL STRUCTURES AS PEOPLE FOUND THEY COULD GROW THEIR FOOD RATHER THAN HAVE TO HUNT FOR IT. FOR THE FIRST TIME EVER, AN ANIMAL WAS NOW ABLE TO CONTROL ITS ENVIRONMENT... US.

Mrs Google hasn't been much help to me in tracking down an insight I'm particularly fond of that says: 'Every generation thinks that those before it were the last ages of innocence'. Maybe if I can't find where it came from I'll just claim it as my own?

Anyway, whoever the quote came from probably wouldn't have been surprised by the stories of the world's lost naivety that various scribes were setting down as they wrote the Torah, the ancient Jewish book of 'Instruction'. While some learned rabbis believe this to be the word of God, as given directly to Moses, other scholars follow a more liberal tradition in thinking that it was an encapsulation of oral folklore. This, they say, would have been handed down over the millennia by people that were expressing their collective hopes and fears as they looked back to the lessons of history.

Those who believe the Torah was created by men say its final version came from as many as four different sources, and that it would have been completed between the 7th and the 5th centuries BCE. It's also known as the Pentateuch because it makes up the first five books of the Old Testament. These sacred texts, when taken together, form the cornerstone of the Judeo-Christian religions.

What does the Torah say? Well, as in the Book of Genesis, the early part of it describes the formation of the Universe. It then moves on to the foundation of our human family… and to the incident that's become known as The Fall of Man. This is the calamity of Adam and Eve, and it tells the sad story of how we departed from the innocence of the earthly paradise that God had intended for us.

But to many anthropologists and religious commentators, what's actually being described is nothing less than an allegory for the upheaval caused by the introduction of agriculture. This was a cultural earthquake that was to make us who we are, because the changes it brought were so great that they wildly accelerated our evolutionary progress. Others, most notably the great geographer and social historian, Jared Diamond, regard it as the 'worst mistake in the history of the human race'.

In describing the origins of mankind, the Adam and Eve tale was drawing heavily on the inherited stories that went back thousands of years to when the first farming and herding societies began to change humans forever. In doing this, the creation story of the Abrahamic faiths has God set his first people, just a single family, to live in contented peace in the beauty of the Garden of Eden. There was only one condition - not to eat from the Tree of the Knowledge of Good and Evil. And we all know where that led.

Western European culture has it that the forbidden fruit was an apple - but this would have been a strange thing to find in the primitive state of Eden as apples were inedible until cultivars were propagated by hybridisation. Perhaps it was an early literary tease, because some scholars believe the choice is a pun on the Latin for evil - malum - and an earlier Greek linguistic root for an apple. The genus is still known as *Malus* today.

Earlier interpretations, however, suggested that the temptation arose from a pomegranate, a fig or a pear. Then again, the Book of Enoch describes the tree as a tamarind, while some ancient rabbinical sources say it was a wine-producing grape. There's even a version that claims it was wheat - but this might be just another ancient gag as the Hebrew word for this is 'khittah' while 'khet' meant sin.

Anyway, whatever it was... we know that the naughty pair nibbled away. God asks them what they're up to and Adam blames Eve, and Eve blames a serpent. As one's schoolmasters used to say, God was 'extremely disappointed with them' and He hands out his eternal punishments for their disobedience: the serpent is condemned to forever walk on its belly, and Eve and all other women, from then on, were sentenced to be the inferior gender, ruled over by men. They would also now know the pain of childbirth.

And Adam? From that time on, God says, he's condemned to give up the life of innocence and ease he'd enjoyed in paradise (which stems from the Persian word for garden, later to become the Greek noun *paradeisos*) and to spend the rest of his days with what the Torah describes as 'sweat on his brow'. God decrees that the very ground he lives on will now be cursed and '... through painful toil you will eat the food from it all the days of your life.'

In other words, Adam was being made to grow things. Divine intervention was no longer going to provide his food, no longer going to just let him pick it off the trees in the way that hunter-gatherers lived in the garden of a natural state. He was going to have to become a farmer. There's little doubting the Torah's intention here of portraying agriculture as a curse on mankind - and one that would be the source of a new age of trouble.

What happened next? Well, Adam and Eve had children - Cain and Abel - and, again, the allegory continues as Cain worked the land while Abel became a hunter and herder of sheep. Farmer Cain then symbolically kills Abel, and with him goes a quarter of the human population. Although Eve would later give birth to girls, this has always presented religious authorities with the unedifying conclusion that the human species was the result of incest and inbreeding.

But the Torah, Genesis, and two later Books of the Pentateuch, then drop into the story another lot of people who'd never been mentioned before. This was a race called the Nephilim, a name that loosely translates as 'giants' in early bibles, a people who were reputed to be so large that they were said to look down on Adam's descendants as 'grasshoppers'.

What are we to make of all this? Needless to say, there's much debate, but many religious scholars and anthropologists are in no doubt that the texts were describing the transitional period between hunter-gathering and the emergence of agriculture. As happened with Adam's people and the Nephilim, they say, the ancient nomadic foragers and hunters were by now interbreeding with the early farming pioneers who were settling down to live in one place.

They also believe that the creation story is looking back to a time when humans were progressing from the simplicity of 'working' a mere fifteen to twenty hours a week as they ate what they found around them - just as modern hunter-gatherers do today - and were moving towards the slog and anxiety of farming life. As to the role of the sexes, The Fall mirrors the transition that took place when the egalitarian division of labour seen in migratory tribes gave way to patriarchal farming societies. Then, as now, these societies had men calling the shots and women staying at home, their movements limited by child rearing and cooking.

If this wasn't a great outcome for women, did it suit anyone else? Almost certainly not, seems to be the conclusion. Research has shown, for example, that compared to the early agricultural settlers, the Nephilim giants of hunter-gatherers would have enjoyed a more varied and nutritious diet, and that this would have made them an average of four inches taller than the pastoralists.

Farming communities were also cursed with the diseases that came with static populations. Unlike the nomadic life, individuals were now living in close proximity to each other - and to their animals. Many scholars, for example, believe that 'the Mark of Cain' that God put upon the first murderer would have been due to the scars that come with smallpox - a variola virus that's contagious in its initial stages and therefore dependent on crowded groups.

Last, unlike the tiny numbers of people in tribal communities, the large towns and cities that sprang up with the introduction of farming would have contained much larger numbers, many of whom would have been unrelated. Like them, Adam and Eve were said to feel shame about being naked, and so wearing clothes became yet another departure from the simpler lives of the hunter-gatherer.

But what was the reality of the revolution that agriculture was supposed to have unleashed? If it really was regarded as such a curse on humanity, why did it ever become so widespread and entrenched?

> **'The agricultural revolution is one of the most controversial events in history.**
> **Some partisans proclaim that it set humankind on the road to**
> **prosperity and progress. Others insist that it led to perdition.'**
> **Yuval Noah Harari, *Sapiens***

We've become so used to measuring evolutionary periods in million year chunks that the point at which agriculture kicked off, around 10,000 years ago, now probably sounds like last Thursday. But we were still very different then. In appearance we would have been recognisable, and we'd certainly have had many of the same memes running about our thought processes. Among other things, these would have given us our deeply held beliefs about the gains that arose from people cooperating. But alongside this would have been the importance of endurance and persistence, the role of language, the power of the imagination, the mechanics of trading, the need for ruling hierarchies, and the efficiencies that came from organising labour.

On the other hand, humans were still living at that time in comparatively small communities where there'd have been strong relationships between the inhabitants, together with a collective fear of outsiders. These group anxieties were partly due to the lack of trust that came from having no recognised property rights to protect them from strangers coming onto their territory, partly down to the Big Man's constant paranoia, and partly because the Dunbar Limit was now being stretched well beyond 150 individuals.

These three things meant that although humans had spread out by then to colonise the entire surface of the globe, there were probably no more than five million or so of us alive at the time. Simply dividing this number by the average community size suggests that there were probably something like 30,000 separate tribes, and no doubt countless different languages. But farming meant things were about to change forever. Agriculture profoundly altered our societies because, as Yuval Harari says in *Sapiens*: 'One on one, even ten on ten, we are embarrassingly similar to chimpanzees. Significant differences begin to appear only when we cross the threshold of 150 individuals, and when we reach 1000 to 2000 individuals the differences are astounding.'

But why did populations grow so much, and how did the social revolution crop up? Why did it then take root? (Even the puns are agricultural.)

There are, of course, a number of theories. First, there was undoubtedly a major change to the climate around this time as the Earth was coming out of an Ice Age, and large areas of the globe were becoming warmer and yet damper. These were ideal conditions for growing the kind of annual plants that die off in the dry season, and leave seeds or tubers dormant until the following year.

Secondly, there's was what became known as the 'dump heap hypothesis' which proposed that wandering tribes would have foraged on the same sites, year after year, and that the penny would have dropped that if you left seeds behind in the ground when you moved on, then edible plants would have sprouted by the next.

But, thirdly, the way that agriculture appears at a number of different places in both the Old and New Worlds around 10,000 years ago suggests that it was simply 'an idea whose time had come.' The light bulbs seemed to go on about then in China, where people began growing rice and millet, in South America with the potato and coca and, most particularly, in what's become known as the Fertile Crescent of the Middle East. This was the region that stretched from the Nile Delta in the west, took a great sweep through what is modern day Israel and Syria, on into southern Turkey, and then down to what geographers would later call Mesopotamia.

A significant proportion of this ancient land was the varied and productive soil between the Tigris and the Euphrates in what's now Iraq. It covered much of what was then known as the Assyrian empire and this included, at the time the Torah was being written, the Kingdom of Judea as a client state. It's the Fertile Crescent that's usually regarded as the cradle of the agricultural revolution because its indiginous plants were to become the founder crops of the modern world - wheat, barley, peas, vetch and flax. Of these wheat was soon being harvested on a large scale.

> 'The Fertile Crescent had a wide range of habitats, from deserts to rich soils to
> snowy mountain tops which created a super abundance of different plant species.'
> Marcus Chown, *What a Wonderful World*

For the first time in the long history of the world, there was now a species that wasn't having to adapt itself to its environment. Quite the opposite - it was using it for its own ends, and even managing to develop it.

But with this breakthrough came the great paradox of agriculture. What we've since come to regard as a slower and more peaceful existence when compared to the hectic speed of our cities, was at that time the reason for a seismic change in the pace of man's existence. Not only were people working 'with sweat on their brow' instead of mooning about picking berries or enjoying a hunt, but farms required many more individuals to make them work than the hunter-gatherer way of life... and before long larger settlements began to spring up. More hands meant more mouths, and the early pioneers quickly discovered that they were able to feed far more people if they worked the land than they ever would have done by randomly hunting over it.

They also soon realised that instead of eating everything that appeared, they now had to plant some of it back to produce the following year's crops. This discovery meant that not only did the soil have to be improved and irrigated - and the only way to do this was to settle close to it - but it also meant that these people had to think strategically as they laid down plans for their futures.

What a tricky meme this must have been for people to have absorbed in the early days of farming. Substituting the freedom of migration and simply picking up whatever you wanted for the difficult, anxious work of land management and animal husbandry was hard enough. But now these farming people were being forced to work round the vagaries of weather, understand the need for crop rotations to get the best out of the soil, and recognise the critical disciplines of doing things at the right time of the year. The seasons suddenly took on ever greater significance, and it's hardly surprising that around now the skin-shedding of the serpent of the Fall began to be represented in Sumerian, Egyptian and even Mesoamerican creation myths as symbolic of the Earth's cycle of death and renewal.

In spite of all this, the benefits that came from agriculture must have made the effort worthwhile. But what were they? What made these pioneers think that farming was a better way of life? Well, first, the settlers found that they were now generating things that could be traded, and the early cereal producers of the plains would have quickly become important people as yields rose and trading routes became established.

Secondly, well-run farms produced more security of food supply than the old ways could ever have done. Regular surpluses now meant settlements were growing so fast that they could support a far greater range of specialised functions. Agricultural communities needed larger numbers of people than the hunter-gatherer communities, and they also required new skills. This led people to start trading not only their produce, but their expertise and labour too.

> **'We did not domesticate wheat, wheat domesticated us.'**
> **Yuval Noah Harari, *Sapiens***

Knowledge about such things as crop management, propagation techniques and methods of selectively breeding animals were becoming extremely valuable. Wild aurochs, for example, were progressively being turned into docile cattle, dangerous boars were domesticated to become the farmyard pig, and feral sheep were tamed - all by removing the more aggressive and dominant individuals.

When archaeologists pore over ancient bone finds they can see how successful this process must have been. Domestication may have led average body sizes to drop as animals were progressively subdued through positive selections, but it also made these once wild animals easier to breed and handle, and then later to slaughter.

On the other hand, draught animals such as the ox and the horse were now being selectively bred for strength and endurance, and soon took over much of the slog of human life by doing the heavy stuff like lifting water and dragging the plough. Before long this kind of progress led to huge increases in the available energy and, in turn, to vastly improved crop yields.

> **'Many anthropologists believe that by gaining power over**
> **animals, humans managed to gain control over the world.'**
> **Marcus Chown, *What a Wonderful World***

Some regions were quicker to exploit animals as beasts of burden than others.

The Middle East had many species to choose from, but the Americas, in particular, were hamstrung by the vandalism of the early settlers. So many large species had been driven to extinction that the absence of candidates to become working animals there became one of the key factors for why their agricultural progress was limited - certainly at a far slower pace than in the Fertile Crescent.

In *Guns, Germs and Steel*, Jared Diamond identifies thirteen species of large animals capable of agricultural work that were domesticated in Eurasia - compared to just one in South America, and none in the rest of the world. Australia was particularly held back by the earlier slaughter, and North America suffered not only from having just the untameable bison to survive the overkill, but also from its paucity of natural grasses for cultivation. Eventually one of them, a wild grain called teosinte, became the iconic Western corn cob, but nobody's too sure how the early farmers would have managed to cultivate it.

Nevertheless, for the first time ever, farming was allowing humans to dominate the other species around them and this, together with their expanding land management techniques, meant they were now controlling their environment. With this came wholly new ideas. It would have been around this time, for instance, that people began to think they had a divine right to rule what they saw.

It's hardly surprising, therefore, that by the time Genesis came to be written, man had enshrined his place in natural law - a landscape in which humans were at the top of the pyramid of life forms and everything else was below them. As Genesis describes it: 'And God said, let us make man in our image, after our likeness: and let them have dominion over the fish of the sea, and over the fowl of the air, and over the cattle, and over all the Earth.'

'Humanity is exalted, not because we are so far above other living
creatures but because knowing them well elevates the very concept of life.'
EO Wilson, *Biophilia*

Greater certainty of production together with the effect of surpluses meant farmers were soon feeding between ten and a hundred times as many people from the same acreage as migratory tribes had ever managed. This was in spite of the nutrition levels of agricultural workers being reduced by the narrower range of foodstuffs.

The consequence of the community's new diets now led to average body sizes dropping, and the general health of farming societies declined as the stresses of following a more organised existence took hold. In addition to these problems, novel diseases were now arising as human populations were spending far longer working in close proximity with their animals.

These and other factors were to lead many anthropologists to suggest that the average woman's body strength would have been reduced to the point where child bearing became far more painful and dangerous than it had been before. Perhaps even in this punishment, the Torah was accurate in predicting God's treatment of Eve.

Was Moses the first person to download from the cloud onto a tablet?

As the farming pioneers pushed on and populations grew, so their collective approach to problem solving led innovation to flourish. Archaeological research has shown, for example, that these early farmers would have quickly worked out how to create more productive strains of plants like barley and wheat. Breakthroughs of this kind meant increased levels of protein and plant carbohydrates, and many of the new hybrids were now able to withstand the storage conditions of the Middle East's dry climate. In turn, this triggered a virtuous circle in production and long-term planning, and new cultivation methods improved to support ever larger communities.

But none of these things can explain why people didn't simply reject the farming life if it was so miserably hard. The old liberties were disappearing, diseases were spreading, agricultural work was laborious, large numbers of people were now being subjugated by others, men were doing the bossing while women had to give up their old equalities to become baby machines. Maybe the lessons of the Torah were right again, and that the freedom and egalitarian lifestyles of the migratory hunter-gatherers were disappearing?

So, why didn't people throw the whole thing into reverse? Why didn't they simply pack it in and return to their previous lives?

The fact was that there was no way back.

With the Dunbar Limit now exceeded, the new towns and cities needed feeding. Their growth had inevitably led to an explosion of specialisms and craft skills. People were now making pottery, leather goods, jewellery, masonry and wooden structures like animal pens - but artisans that could produce these things would have lost the old knowledge to live off the land. And craftsmen weren't the only ones who'd come to depend on others. Wholly new occupations had also grown up with society's booming scale, and people were now emerging with specialised roles such as bakers, brewers, priests, physicians, musicians, mystics, storytellers and poets.

> **'Early farming spread not because rational individuals prefer to farm,**
> **but because farming communities with particular institutions**
> **beat mobile hunter-gatherer populations in intergroup competitions.'**
> **Joseph Heinrich, *The WEIRDest People in the World***

Barter and exchange was thriving, skills and specialisations were in demand, and professional types simply wouldn't have known how to revert to the self-sufficiency of small numbers. Not only would the know-how have been lost, but however tough the new kinds of work might have been, the system worked. Food surpluses led on to yet further specialisations, to more skilled people and, in turn, this generated more trading, more competition, more innovation, more energy gains, more organisation, more cultural complexity, more complicated hierarchies and, alongside all this, to ever higher demands for workers.

What's also clear from the lessons of evolutionary history is that when revolutionary changes result in non-zero gains, then no organism ever seems to go backwards. In particular, we humans don't uninvent things: we adjust, we adapt, and our new knowledge goes deep into our brains' hardwiring, getting passed on from one generation to the next without so much as a backwards glance.

Alongside these advances, though, halfway houses grew up between the lost freedoms and the settled communities. Fruit growing and the propagation of nut bearing trees bridged the worlds of foraging and farming. Tribes of pastoral herders moved from hunting towards migratory animal driving. These sorts of people were continuously on the move in the search for secure grazing and, as they travelled, they opened up trading routes, bringing with them not only fresh meat and other animal products, but also the benefits of common languages and the spread of customs and cultures.

> **'Men are not so much the keeper of herds as herds are the keepers of men.'**
> **Henry David Thoreau, *Walden***

As these pastoralists intermarried with people they met along the way, so they also passed on their genes. As Adam Rutherford says in *A Brief History of Everyone Who Ever Lived*: 'Genes change cultures, culture changes genes. Farming has been arguably the single greatest force in changing human culture and biology.'

And the new ways certainly weren't all bad. Interaction between strangers grew, territorial paranoia declined, food security improved, infant mortality was reduced, and the increases in non-zero gains from trading meant things that had previously been considered luxuries now became expected staples.

The scale of the new settlements were also incentivising people to defend what they'd built. As villages and towns became more organised, random violence from neighbouring tribes would have declined. Some commentators have even said that minor crimes such as theft would have reduced around this time as it was plainly harder to steal a field of wheat than it was to take a dead deer or a string of beads.

And alongside these advances came profound new thought processes and assumptions.

First, the notion that humans now had the skills to exploit their surroundings was being tempered by the problems they couldn't control. With things like climate change, unusual weather events, fluctuating river levels and the dangers of wild animals came new myths and beliefs to explain them. Polytheism took root as everything in these people's lives became infused with meaning and gods. And because the intentions of the gods needed to be pacified, and traded for reverence and devotion, so superstition set up home in our hardwiring. It's with us still - just try saying how much you're hoping for something to happen without looking round for a piece of wood to touch.

Secondly, as land that had once been as free as the wind to the hunter-gatherer became cultivated and productive, so man's symbolic relationship with his surroundings was developing into a deep psychological bond. Yes, of course he was putting a lot of himself into farming, but he was getting a lot back as well. Not only was the boom in the population rewarding his efforts - and his gene pool - but, for the first time ever, the land he was investing so much time and effort in was becoming valuable.

With this happening alongside the rise of individual crafts, societies began to stratify into winners and losers. A landowning class grew up, the haves looked down on the have-nots, men dominated women, the pale skinned looked down on the dark as field labourers were little better than slaves, and things like intelligence, education and ingenuity were becoming rewarded as society's hierarchies mushroomed.

Thirdly, the status of the Big Man was also inexorably growing. Initially he'd probably have resisted the move to sedentary lifestyles because his power came from micromanaging the individuals in his tribe on what to believe, where to hunt, and how to behave. He'd therefore have viewed rising numbers with alarm because keeping a tight control over his people would have become harder to impose. Now, if power was shifting to the wealthy new landowners, what was he to do?

He needn't have worried. With bigger settlements came entirely new opportunities for chucking his weight around. More integrated yet complex trading had brought with it hugely increased opportunities for zero sum behaviour, and along with this had come natural extensions into such trust-breaking activities as cheating and stealing. The Big Man now began to earn his corn by introducing laws, resolving disputes, organising hierarchies and governance systems, enforcing justice and handing down punishments. These sorts of things gave him a whole new legitimacy that drove the memes around his authority to go even deeper than they'd been before. Opinions about him were now based less on his fictional origins, and more on the population's increasing need for social order.

With his growing importance, however, also came the problems of power. Worrying issues began to break out repeatedly due to jealous cronies, partisan coteries, families fracturing into cliques, land grabbing and the hundred and one other things that make the ruling classes go bad. The notion of structured societies and the rule of law may have been firmly planted into our brains around this time, but so too were the dangers of nasty things like the seizing of power, factionalism, lying, betrayal, disloyalty and the short-term success of violence.

Above all, what seemed to stick in our brains most was that worldly success led to power... and power led to fecundity. The better off you were, the more attractive you now became. And this meant that the more your genes were passed on, the more you increased your family numbers and your top-down version of natural selection. More status meant more wives and more sex. With women reduced to sucking up to powerful men, and agriculture and cities now established, so the big cheeses took to investing in their bloodlines and the creation of their dynasties.

As communities grew, the importance of one's relations and clan ties became ever more important. Success for one's family now meant getting *other* people to carry out the hard, sweaty business of producing food and becoming darker, while the winners stayed pale, sending out the visual message that they were at the top of the heap. Before long, the most obvious way of measuring one's progress in these hard-working farming societies was... by not having to do the hard work.

Strong forces were underpinning these new evolutionary currents. Perhaps most importantly was the growth of religions that could make sense of the unpredictable. And, as they did so, they unified people by laying down what would become accepted myths and memes. Among the most important of these were the cornerstone dogmas that supported the Big Man's right to rule. With the enthusiastic support of the rulers, a priest caste now quickly rose up to sit among the winners, and together they gazed down at the cowed poplace below. There wasn't much push-back to this because as people followed increasingly complicated lives, they became ever more dependent on the assurances of supernatural powers, and on trusting the ruling class who were, supposedly, the agents of their gods' will on earth.

The mass cooperation networks that developed in larger communities, and the gains that came from people trading their occupations and skills now needed a script. Unsurprisingly, this didn't take long to arrive as religious teachers, prophets and the other imagined orders of authority stepped up to explain how people should behave. Divisions might be widening in societies, but people were now increasingly being told why certain sections of society were becoming dominant or suppressed, seen as allies or were discriminated against, and these instructions were coming from the gods - as interpreted by priests and shamen - and all of them somehow entwined with the ruler's legends and mythologies.

These kinds of stories were extremely potent. They told everyone that there were natural reasons for such things as success or failure in life, and where people should be on the ladder of life. These rungs were now being explained as due to such divinely ordained features as one's caste, class, family, ancestors, origins or even a previous incarnation. Memes about pecking orders - and the need to maintain them - settled ever more deeply in our minds in ways that had never been necessary in the tiny, egalitarian, hunter-gatherer societies.

Religious certainties, a ruling elite, landowners and a successful merchant class all began to come together to ensure agricultural societies were run by a pyramidal command structure. As they mixed together, so each of the different sources of authority now supported the claims of the others. Grain, for example, was allocated to the temples, prayers were said to the gods that controlled the weather, farming riches went to the rulers as taxes. And, by 4,500 BCE, there were entire layers of bureaucratic elites supervising society's output.

Children were increasingly being brought up and educated to have this system drummed into their heads. The idea of a central government was established. All good, you might think as this would produce order and an ethical culture. But of course the different interests that made this possible proved to be fluid and changeable. Inevitably there was any amount of sliding around of alliances, jealousies, mistrust, greed and every other nasty power grab that led to people jockeying for position. It was the beginning of the underlying instability of complex societies that's defined mankind's history ever since.

How did Big Men keep the show on the road? As ever, with presumption, suppression, violence and an occasional smattering of hand-outs. Naturally, as the larger communities grew, it didn't take them long to work out that the best insurance policy was to surround oneself with hired muscle. And doubtless the people who stepped up to provide this strong-arm stuff were exactly the kinds of arrogant ruffians who thought that they, too, were above manual labour. One can imagine them strutting around, avoiding too much sweaty work and, because they depended on the Big Man's favours and support, being only too happy to put down any kind of muttering there might have been about his parasitism, or right to rule.

These thugs, and even the trained militia the Big Man would also have developed, knew that their job was to keep the lid on dissent. The approach unquestionably worked, but it would also prove to be dangerously counter-productive because once the bullies had cowed a population into obedience, there was then very little else for them to do. To fill in the time, they bullied unnecessarily and so encouraged enmity as they swanked around, acting tough and encouraging myths about what invincible warriors they were.

This would be all right for a bit, but problems arose because once they'd been hired, they were then almost impossible to fire. It was a very brave king indeed who'd try and thin down a well-armed bunch of violent goons. This meant he had to be careful - because if soldiers and bodyguards had too little to do, they might start giving him funny looks. They, in turn, could also start getting funny looks because the citizens they were pushing around weren't slow to realise who was stumping up the tax revenue for this lot to be quite so unpleasantly parasitic.

These sorts of factors had to be among the main reasons for the second great consequence of larger societies - the temptation for rulers to pick fights with their neighbours. Put bluntly, monarchs would have had all these bragging soldiers hanging around, so why not use them for a little warfare? After all, what could make a Big Man's head swell more than crushing a lot of unbelieving enemies, showing everyone that the other lot's religions were wrong, and annihilating their myths?

Looked at from our historical perspective, hierarchical cultures that were based on the imagined orders of interwoven religions, divinely ordained rulers, and obedient soldiers may not appear to have the same claim to power that the day-to-day survival skills that Big Men had relied on in hunter-gatherer societies.

Nonetheless the system plainly worked. They used to say that one priest could do the work of a hundred soldiers, but the energy gains generated by the agricultural revolution were becoming so set in society's memes that teachers could now take over the job of enshrining the status quo. As Tom Paine was to later say in *The Age of Reason*: 'One good schoolmaster is of more use than a hundred priests.'

What lay behind all this? Why would the vastly larger numbers of oppressed workers put up with a power structure that had all the contributors at the bottom, and all the layabouts at the top? Yet again evolutionary theorists can see the same set of factors coming through that are repeatedly seen in the natural world. In both Nature and our own societies, gains that result from symbiotic relationships can be judged to be so critical to one's survival… that it's even worth putting up with being the subordinate, exploited party.

So while the peasant class probably made up something like 95% of these early populations, even the lowest orders must have thought they were getting enough benefits to have supported a system in which Big Men were taking so much. In spite of this, a few of the more thoughtful rulers might have recognised that some kind of social contract was necessary, and the more enlightened would have taken care to throw a bone every now and then in the general direction of those below them.

The growth in trading and competition in the new kinds of settled societies were by now encouraging a culture of innovation and progress. Ingenuity and skills were becoming valued, and this sometimes made it possible for a particularly talented individual to advance, usually through inventing a better way of doing something.

As communities expanded, so increased numbers of brains were being utilised, and as this happened, the chances of finding improvements mushroomed. Inventions now began to arise that profoundly improved the energy efficiencies of farming societies. Someone invented the wheel (although as Sid Caesar said: '... he was an idiot, the guy who invented the other three was a genius'), a harness that didn't choke a draught animal, the optimal shape for effective ploughs, a contained screw that could raise water and, of course, ways of smelting durable metals, all now began to come through as the impact of agriculture defined our human existence.

'The revolution in agricultural technology made society more secure and more dense in numbers - the more people the more brain. Breakthroughs led to more breakthroughs (and these) would in time lead to yet newer inventions and yet greater productivity - which in turn led to further specialisation and so the cycle continued.'
Robert Wright, *Nonzero*

In spite of all this, did the hierarchical structures mean that people would be prepared to put up with social inequalities forever? No, of course not, and questions about whether individuals or groups were getting their fair share of the community's gains would have started around now. And they've continued ever since. Even today, the forces that create society's pecking order are a subject of constant review. Entire philosophical and political movements rise up and fall back as society evolves and different eras see people attempt to bring about more equitable balances.

Agriculture might have been what lit the fuse of so much cultural change, but it was to be the use of metal that hurtled it forward. The mining of ores had begun surprisingly early with copper being processed around 5,000 BCE, gold from about 2,500 and then bronze a further 500 years after that. And it was this last discovery that was to arguably be the most critical of the breakthroughs - because it wasn't long before an early genius found that by combining it with other metals, he could make things that were stronger and longer-lasting. It was at this point that even inanimate materials were being made to cooperate symbiotically.

The game changer, however, probably came along some time around 1,500 BCE when wrought iron was first invented. This first happened somewhere in the Fertile Crescent, but it was rapidly taken up in Western Europe. The Chinese then refined the technology further by discovering how to cast it - and the discovery led on to infinitely more powerful implements being made from ever stronger materials.

Tools became more complex and specific. Things like the angled plough, stirrups that allowed a riding archer to wield a bow, and sharp swords that were to become weapons of mass destruction. The harrow and the waterwheel followed, and as yields and conquest soared, the scale of cities soared. Yet more specialised jobs were being created, skills flourished, might became right, trading routes developed - and all of this combined to see societies become ever more stratified.

But is it possible you're wondering what had happened to the hunter-gatherers while all this progress was being made? Where were the Nephilim now? Well, these original people must have continued to live alongside the farming pioneers because even centuries later they were still regarded as a nuisance. The Book of Jubilees, for example, is clear that eliminating them as competition to farmers was God's main aim when he decided to flood the Earth so that Noah's people could thrive.

Rather more prosaically, the hunter-gatherer tribes were pushed to the margins. Their numbers were reduced - and there they've stayed, largely unchanged, leading their simple lives and being studied by people like Daniel Everett and Jared Diamond. They, like so many anthropologists before them, hail them as examples to us all.

Yet the forces that should have been taking *H. sapiens* forwards to ever richer civilisations were still being held back. This was because societies were still reliant on verbal understandings, and without ways of recording data, or having binding agreements, money was missing to balance their bargains. In the absence of prescribed, written laws, communities were always going to suffer the social problems that arose from misunderstandings, to say nothing of the intentional deceptions and revolts that would have been so widespread.

Without having recorded communication, and with dodgy types able to deny they'd said things, there was always going to be a 'trust barrier' to be jumped before people could rely on iron-clad covenants. It was critical to overcome these obstacles.

But how?

Filthy lucre... but it had a surprisingly
moralising effect.

CHAPTER TEN

HOW WERE PEOPLE GOING TO FIND WAYS OF ESTABLISHING TRUST IN SOCIETIES THAT HAD NOW GROWN SO LARGE THAT IT WAS IMPOSSIBLE TO KNOW EVERYONE? THE ANSWER CAME WITH THE SIXTH REVOLUTION - THE USE OF OUTSOURCED TRUST WITH THE INVENTION OF THINGS LIKE NUMBERS, WRITING AND MONEY. IT WAS TIME FOR THE 'BRAIN OUTSIDE THE BRAIN.'

Perhaps the most startling realisation about the currents in the 'ocean of life' is that they're so constant, so uniform and just so immutable.

But why's that?

Well, going right back to our origins, the Laws of Thermodynamics mean that at the heart of all life forms is the demand for energy. It has to come from somewhere. Every living thing needs it to survive, and then uses it to stay alive long enough to reproduce. By managing to hang on to it, the most successful organisms get to stay one step ahead of the threats that are coming from other things… because they, of course, are always trying to take it away from them.

The trick that organisms constantly try to pull off is to use this precious energy for themselves, rather than seeing it stolen by others, or seeping away as a result of entropic forces. Yet the repeated theme of evolution is that different things will get together to divide tasks up. By not having to do everything for themselves, they become more complex and yet more efficient. And by being efficient they get to share in the energy gains.

This explains the great paradox of life… that organisms may be using competition to overcome the 1st Law… but they also have to employ cooperation to overcome the 2nd. Yes, living things are grabbing each others' energy through being horribly competitive… but it is cooperation, and specialisation and exchange, that leads to the 1+1=3 mechanism that means everything's not then lost to entropy. Martin Nowak summed this up in his book, *Supercooperators* when he wrote: 'Cooperation arises out of competition, even though the two are locked together in ceaseless conflict.'

As ever, behind it all is the selfish gene: doing its job by making sure that life survives by adapting its vehicles to meet whatever needs to be done.

Within our human story, these exact same currents were becoming ever more evident in the ways the agricultural revolution was leading us to evolve. We, too, look for 1+1=3 relationships as the division of labour frees up time and energy for humans in precisely the same way it does in the natural world.

And with trading routes now established, and farming and pastoral migration settled as a way of life, it was becoming increasingly obvious that having skills that could be exchanged for other things was a huge winner. Not only did it put bread on the table, but the fair division it then produced led on to calmer and more efficient societies. So great were the advantages of following this model, it now seemed, that it was even worth running the occasional risk of being cheated.

By 7,000 or so years ago, farming had acted as a fast-acting catalyst, incentivising individuals to join up in ever larger societies, and to form superorganisms in exactly the way that the specialisation of cells had created advanced bodies. In a parallel action to the ways these cells evolved their functions through symbioses, agricultural communities were soon seeing winners, but also losers and suppressed citizens who were grudgingly accepting social inequalities in return for rewards such as security and a sense of belonging. Yet in an extraordinary repeat of genetic evolution, it was at this point that humans began to run into the same problems that other species had been forced to overcome.

What was our particular roadblock? It was the ever growing danger that large numbers of people were being overly exploited. Other things in Nature had overcome the issue with a mixture of productive mistakes, mutations and millions of years of refinement - but what were we going to come up with? *You* might be trustworthy was always the problem... but was the other man? Sound familiar? I guess so, because we still face the same question at every twist and turn of our daily lives today... and that's in the largely law abiding, ethical, organised, review writing and trouble free times that we have now.

But these things were far more difficult to solve in the emerging agricultural communities. Societies had become so large by now that there was no way of knowing everyone, and certainly no way of weighing up their motives. The Dunbar Limit of hunter-gatherer colonies may have held back progress, but the reason for its ceiling on numbers was now clear... it was set by how many individuals one could know in enough depth to form judgements about whether they could be trusted.

And so, as these new agricultural societies refined themselves into top-down, command-driven hierarchies, people began to run huge risks by specialising their labour. Exploitation and wrong-doing must have been rife, and community's stability was constantly being challenged by lawlessness. As for an individual's chances of surviving on his own if something went wrong, then there'd have been little chance of him reverting to the previous ways of foraging and hunting. Non-zero cooperation might have been terrific, but there were cheats everywhere who were exploiting the strategy's weakness.

> 'If everybody always lies to you, the consequence isn't that you
> believe the lies, but rather that nobody believes anything any longer.'
> Hannah Arendt, *The Origins of Totalitarianism*

The old days had been easier. In small societies a person's reputation for being a taker or a wrong 'un became known very quickly. In larger ones, however, there were always new suckers coming along, and stratified social structures meant that people at the top tended to protect each other. The unpleasant upshot of all this was that as human interaction was settling into its new model, these same societies were now in danger of institutionalising uncaring, devious and exploitative tactics.

What had to be found were ways of outsourcing solutions - mechanisms that everyone could sign up to, and which wouldn't be open to later disagreements or shyster fact twisting. We needed what anthropologists would later describe as a 'brain outside the brain'... things that could be trusted to record facts rather than opinions, and which would reduce the chances of people coming off badly in deals.

In other words, people needed written laws that everyone could understand, contracts that spelt out individual responsibilities, ways of counting that were universally recognised, formal records about what people said and agreed to. And a mechanism that could even out the imbalances in trading exchanges.

Easier said than done. In fact, achieving all this was downright tricky.

The first problem with coming up with some kind of external brain was that the idea swam against the same forces of cultural evolution that had brought about command and control hierarchies in the first place. After all, systems that favoured the powerful were designed to keep most of their subjects either enslaved or in the dark. So why would the Big Man have ever allowed the unwashed to share in universally available information?

The answer, almost certainly, was that the downsides never occurred to him. Knowledge was power and if the peasants never understood how to use it, then this could only be yet another way of keeping them in their place.

So when and why did recorded information first kick-off? First out of the blocks was probably money, because the idea of having some kind of balancing item for unequal barters almost certainly predates written history. Tally sticks, for example, and things like cowry shells and notched bones, have been found that go back to pre-agricultural times.

But the concept of 'representative money' in which, as David Graeber puts it in *Debt: The First 5,000 Years*: 'I owe you' progresses to 'I owe you one unit of something' probably appeared initially in the advanced societies of Mesopotamia. This fugitive concept of delayed reward was a colossal breakthrough, because it managed to find a way of overcoming the 'coincidence of wants' that had always held back the opportunities for swaps and barter. It was also a way of shortcutting the time-consuming process that the bargaining procedure demanded. As Elon Musk would later say: 'Money is just data that allows us to avoid the inconvenience of barter.'

Graeber argues that economies in which articles weren't sold or traded, but valued for their own inherent worth, would have splintered away from crude exchanges quite early in these agrarian societies. The barrier the idea jumped was for people to make the enormous leap of faith in which both parties could agree that some kind of token could represent a claim, say, on a flock of sheep or a load of grain in a warehouse.

An even more mind-bending leap then came later, when people created metal versions of these tokens, and they ultimately became coins. Now, not only would these have needed a complete faith in the system, but they also required a rare knowledge of mining and refining. Only by knowing what effort had gone into making them could metal coins have ended up providing the basis for people's assessment of intrinsic value.

The inherent faith one needs in the notion of money has lodged deeply in us as a cultural meme. It's a belief that must have begun as agricultural communities expanded, yet by the time of the Roman Empire it had even entered into the language with credit meaning 'he trusts', and debit meaning 'he owes'.

As for numbers and mathematics, the first attempts at creating sophisticated systems that could establish deals probably came at around the same time that people were trying to write things down. Both grew out of the bureaucratic compulsion to record stuff, and were probably sparked off around 3,500 BCE, some six thousand years after the origins of agricultural societies.

In many ways it's surprising that getting to this point took such a long time. One can only conclude that there'd have been difficult problems to overcome, but also that trading surpluses weren't so complicated, or conducted over such long distances, that they demanded sophisticated solutions.

Whatever led up to the issues, it must have been around now that places like the Sumer city-states of Ur and Uruk - both in what's now Southern Iraq - would have contained tens of thousands of inhabitants. And they all needed governing. These two great trading centres were only something like fifty kilometres apart, but they and their satellite towns would have required trusted communications systems to document what went where, and who owed what to whom. Archaeologists have found extensive evidence that the sorts of things that were being handled included the earliest records for registering the sales of… different kinds of beer. It's always the vital things in life that drive change.

Ticks and straight lines first started appearing as ways of making records on clay tablets around now, both in Mesopotamia and further west in Egypt. No doubt these were clumsy attempts to begin with, but they still preceded similar progress in other parts of the world by thousands of years. Compared to them, the first numerals in China didn't get going for another two millennia, and progress was even slower in India and the Americas.

As the scale and complications of trading grew, so the need for larger, group numbers became more apparent. Base 10 began to be widely used - presumably because it stemmed from the number of fingers we have. The Romans would even call them 'digits'. Larger numbers could then be described by supplementing single figures with the practice of adding words in front that represented multiples, just as we have today for 'twenty', 'thirty' and so on.

Interestingly, base 10 wasn't always the accepted order. Three quite different cultures adopted base 12 systems and this idea has persisted down to us, even today, in the number of inches in a foot, months in a year, or hours in the day. Like 10, 12 is a highly composite number and some cultures, particularly the Babylonians, adopted a multiple of this in the use of base 60. Once again, this has echoes for us in our measurements of the passage of time, seconds and minutes, the angles in a circle, and the degrees of a compass.

These base systems were cumbersome, however, and although they had a symbol that marked the end of a collection of numbers, they all suffered from not having a zero. This made them unsuitable for arithmetical computations and it wasn't until the Hindus used a vacant circle - *sunya* in Sanskrit - that the idea of having something to show where the power of the base wasn't occurring came to mean more than just the end of a complex series.

Before this arrived it was impossible, for instance, to tell if the writer would have meant 8.02, 820 or 8020. The only way one could have guessed at it was by understanding the context. The Islamic world later translated *sunya* into *sifr*, and this ultimately morphed into 'cipher' to mean zero.

The zero solution to the perfected positional system had so many advantages that base 10 went on to become the universal language of numbering in pretty much every region and culture. Thousands of years later the Greeks took the concept of named numbers further when they used the initials of their words for them as a shorthand. These became the 'attic' numerals of the ancient world, and they were widely used until they were themselves overtaken by Rome putting its usual fingerprints over everyone else's culture.

Some historians argue that the letters that represent Roman numbers had pictorial origins. The V for five, for example, was said to represent the fingers of an open hand and the X, for ten, arose from two of these, one on top of another. The L, C and M were adaptations of the original Greek forms and the D for five hundred was a half version of an earlier notation for a thousand.

The numeric symbols we use these days are reckoned to be Hindu-Arabic, and while their origins probably date back to the Ashoka inscriptions of the 3rd century BCE, the final forms were the result of a kind of informal lingua franca that was used by the merchants lining the trading routes to the East.

When it came to the invention of writing, the idea of setting things down for someone else to interpret was almost certainly intertwined with the use of numbers. The two different ways of recording information were thought to have emerged at roughly the same time, and both of them first arose in the major cities of the Fertile Crescent.

Did people see the beauty of poetic expression or the perfection of quadratic equations when they were developing these systems? No, probably not, and instead they were simply methods of keeping records: just ways of improving administrative efficiencies and of tracking economies. No doubt there were people fiddling their expenses even then.

Originally the idea of non-verbal communication had been pictorial, and went back as far as the earliest cave drawings. Images like these depicted real-life events, and as with all visual art they were 'read' at a glance. The progression from there to a person looking at individual letters that joined up to make words, and from there on to understanding the collective meaning of sentences, needed huge intellectual leaps. And of course, it required the writer to know that the reader would be part of the same double act.

It's hardly surprising, therefore, that the original attempts at writing were only used by tiny sections of society, made up almost certainly of members of the priest caste and the higher echelons of government. Nonetheless, the process of moving from a picture to a series of words that were slowly absorbed by the reader, involved a long transitional period before alphabetical or phonetic writing systems took off.

The Sumerians were probably the first people to overcome the problem when they developed arrangements that represented the sound of spoken words as marks pressed into wet clay. This was then fired in an oven for posterity. These marks were made with a reed stylus that had been cut into a wedge and the shape - cuneus is the Latin for wedge - became known as cuneiform script.

Scribes were highly regarded craftsmen who were said to swagger about with a collection of these angled reeds slung from their belts - rather like the petty officials who used to have a row of pen clips hanging over their breast pockets. But these early record keepers must have earned their bragging rights because they became so skilled at producing cuneiform scripts that it quickly evolved into a wide range of representative shapes and interpretive options.

At much the same time as this, roughly 3,000 BCE, the idea of connecting pictograms was also flowering in the hands of the ancient Egyptians. They'd developed the idea of combining symbols into hieroglyphs, a great advance because the approach had the advantage of pictures making some kind of sense in themselves, and yet they could also suggest deeper meanings because of the ways they were arranged.

Archaeologists tend to regard these various transitional systems as 'proto-writing' in that they were largely limited to recording bureaucratic information. This usually meant that there was nothing in them to convey nuance. Instead, they were simply another of the screw-turning activities that were being used to separate the bosses from the peasants.

The Chinese, incidentally, had developed a quite separate writing system that emerged from their addiction to divination. The old con men (apologies, clairvoyant mystics) convinced people they could see the future by scratching marks on oracle bones and eggs, and then heating them up to see how they cracked.

It was a bit like the old biddies that would read the soggy leaves at the bottom of a teacup: '... look, there's a boat. You'll be going on a journey!' But this then progressed to the Chinese fortune tellers thinking: 'hang on, that actually does look like a boat' and, from there on, they began to link line drawings with words and expressions.

The transition away from using pictograms, and towards systems where the eye would scan along a sequence of individual letters that combined to form a word, only emerged after another intermediate stage. This happened when simple drawings were made to stand for the sounds of spoken words. Historians call these symbols 'phonograms' and the great advantage of them was that they began to convey dynamic meaning - whether things were coming or going - as well as being a huge leap forward in being able to convey more precise connotations.

This breakthrough idea would have started around 2,500 BCE, and because it marked the point at which record keeping progressed to the first glimmerings of complex communication, rhythm, emotion and even imaginative description, anthropologists point to it as the birth of literature.

But the concept also had the inherent problem that there were many words that had much the same sound when they were spoken - but which carried quite different meanings. These are called homophones and while, even today, most languages still have lots of them, the context in which they're used makes the meaning clear. We don't have much trouble, for example, sorting out whether someone means 'by, bye or buy' when they're talking, but the early scribes would certainly have had lots of problems when they were writing them down.

The big step that overcame this was when people came up with an agreed alphabet, a neat solution that probably emerged from the priestly scripts of Egypt. The idea then evolved in the hands of the great merchants of Phoenicia - roughly where Lebanon is today - because they'd have used their trading empires to make a standard approach universally accepted.

'The advent of the written word around 3,300 BC lifted history's curtain and revealed an already well-established pattern of long-distance trade, not only in luxury and strategic goods, but in bulk staples such as grain and timber as well.'
William Bernstein, *A Splendid Exchange, How Trade Shaped the World*

The Phoenicians gave their name to the phonetic alphabet, and although they probably first just used it for bookkeeping, it proved to be such a strong solution to the Sumerian homophone problems that it was quickly taken up for other uses. The Book of Exodus, for example, even has Moses telling his sidekicks to use it to account for the materials that had been used when they'd made the Tabernacle.

What did these ancient people do once the notion had taken root that writing could take the place of oral traditions? Very few of them would have been able to read, of course, but the ruling classes pretty quickly cottoned on to how powerful the written word could be in getting their elites to spread a consistent version of their creation myths. This was too good an opportunity to resist and it now became an important way of establishing the memes they needed for telling their subjects about their right to rule - vital credibility to underline their power.

And so it was that a new art form of poetic writing was used to create the earliest surviving literature. The first of these was a record of the divine background to Uruk's king in *The Epic of Gilgamesh* - a rattling good read but something that also described his greatness, his origins and his quest for the meaning of life. Within it were stories of the gods and heroes of Mesopotamia, and the culture of its people. It was a statement of the king and the city's glory… and it established an entirely new concept called history.

'With writing you could suddenly create extremely long and intricate stories, which were stored on tablets and papyri rather than in human heads.'
Yuval Noah Harari, *Homo Deus*

At around this time, 2,100 BCE, Uruk was a sophisticated place spread across something like two square miles and having over 50,000 inhabitants. It was intensely stratified socially and divided into grids of streets and canals with neighbourhoods of specialised craftsmen. So wealthy was it that precious metals and stones were sent long distances to adorn its ruling class. It was worth boasting about - and King Gilgamesh

'Now hear this!' The wagging finger
of the *Code of Hammurabi*'.

would have wanted you to know it. As Thomas Carlyle was later to say: 'No great man lives in vain. The history of the world is but the biography of great men.'

Ur, meanwhile, was equally as large, if not more so, and The Book of Genesis records it as the birthplace of Abraham. Roughly fifty years after the *Epic* had been written, the king there, Ur-Nammu, found his own use for the power of the written word. In his case it wasn't to be used for self-glorification, but as a mechanism to formalise his authority.

> 'The histories of mankind are histories of the higher classes.'
> Thomas Malthus, *An Essay on the Principle of Population*

He recorded his system of governance and justice as the *Code of Ur-Nammu*, and in doing so he created the first statements ever seen of Sumerian law. While this was, literally, written in stone for some two hundred years or so, it set the benchmark for

The Secrets of Life - Book Two

the more famous *Code of Hammurabi*, which was named after the king of Uruk who was reigning around 1,810 BCE.

This latter code makes for astonishing reading. At roughly the time that the ancient Britons were piling up boulders to make Stonehenge, King Hammurabi was laying down 282 specific laws that gave detailed directions for establishing contracts, recording the terms of transactions, spelling out legal liabilities, the balance of blame in divorces, punishments for adultery, perjury, different types of theft and any number of other social infractions, each with its place on a scale of penalties. Most of these, needless to say, were gruesome.

Grisly though they might be, the *Code* laid down the principle of the presumption of innocence and the importance of evidence. It denied Ur-Nammu's view of matched retribution - 'an eye for an eye' - and instead introduced the more unsettling principle that position in the social hierarchy was key to one's legal status. The higher up you were, the lighter seemed to be society's view of your need to be punished. In spite of this, both codes still rank as breathtakingly sophisticated systems.

The Sumerian region was later to implode into warfare, and split between the Assyrians in the north and the Babylonians in the south. As this was happening, the growth of the written language was moving from the Middle East to Europe. The Greeks took the various systems on, and by the time of Homer, they'd replaced the Phoenicians as the standard bearers of progress. Among other things, they brought the first two Hebrew letters of Aleph and Beth into their own language, as Alpha and Beta, and then joined them together and established the concept of the 'alphabet'.

A further Greek advance was to introduce specific symbols for vowel sounds and, as societies progressed, so European scripts split into the Runic, Gothic and Cyrillic alphabets. Similarly, the Aramaic ones fractured into Hebrew and Arabic, while others went further afield into the Brahmic and Mongolian scripts.

The languages of the Orient, meanwhile, were doing things differently. They had never developed the concept of limiting the number of letters, and instead adopted systems in which thousands of characters and complex signs were non- linguistic and usually pictorial. They were to later evolve into representing words for objects and even whole phrases and, in so doing, they acquired what's known as 'logogramic' value.

But if numbers, mathematics, writing systems and cartography were evolving as separate and sophisticated versions of the same essential solution, then the meaning of money was also evolving at the same time. To some historians, what would later be described as 'commodity money' was coming through to represent the inherent value of an asset, and this was therefore seen as an extension of market activity. The shekel, for example, was both a specific weight of barley as well as its equivalent in the metallic value of a coin.

The other interpretation of progress is known as the 'credit theory of money' in which the currency itself took on a value. This, naturally, placed a greater burden on the individual if people were to have trust in each other... and it also required them to buy into the idea that mere coins and paper could represent wealth.

Perhaps there was a crossover period between the two schools of thought when precious metals like gold and silver began being used as coinage? The worry with these, however, was always that the surface of the coin could cover up baser metals beneath it, but the idea shot forward when touchstones were discovered that could measure the amount and quality of gold within alloys. Once faith in their purity grew, governments began to stamp emblems of one side and their rulers' heads on the other as a way of guaranteeing their weight.

But trust a government? You've got to be kidding... and debasing the currency became a much-used mechanism of misrule. This practice may have cut its teeth in the ancient world, but sadly it continues right down to the present day with money printing and hyperinflation in places like Zimbabwe and Venezuela.

> **'Military and political power came to rely on materials and services provided by merchants who responded to market forces rather than bureaucratic commands. Slowly, the top down Big Man model gave way to the logic of the market. Why? Because of decentralised data control. Interestingly, better writing, easier alphabets and user-friendly scripts all evolved around this time. By the second millennium coined money emerged and spread because markets were outpacing command economies and becoming normalised.'**
> **Robert Wright, *Nonzero***

The individual's version of this kind of organised cheating was called money clipping. Coins at that time were very rarely perfectly round and people used to shave the edges off and then melt down the sliced bits to counterfeit new ones. Another trick was to take some of the gold or silver out of a coin and then carefully replace it with cheaper metals. This racket accounts for the bit in the movie where somebody bites into a coin, trying to find out whether its hardness seems to be right.

The Secrets of Life - Book Two

None of these crimes were regarded lightly. Since money was a form of contract or guarantee, removing the ingredient of trust from it was seen to be one of society's worst crimes. And it was often, I'm afraid, punishable by death.

Forms of commodity money left their mark on the language. The rarity of salt, for example - *sal* in Latin - retains an echo in salary. Being broke, impecunious, was derived from *pecus* for cattle, and even the *capita* of capital assets had its origins as a measure of how many heads of farm animals one owned.

> **'What investment banking is to the ambitious and acquisitive today, the
> pepper trade was to the Romans - the most direct route to great riches.'**
> **Yuval Noah Harari, *Homo Deus***

Money gradually left its intrinsic, commodity-based roots behind, and as the distance from barter to true commerce increased… so people were being asked to trust in the external brain even more than they believed in the issuer. Guarantees were only as good as the rulers that stood behind the stated value, and the profound human need to depend on this broke down the barriers between people and cultures in a way that no amount of wars or religions could ever have imagined.

As Yuval Noah Harari describes in his great book, *Sapiens*: 'The trust in money proved to be so strong that it transcended peoples who hated and despised each other, held religious differences and operated foreign empires… why? Because while religions ask us to believe in something, money only asks us to believe in something that other people already believe in.'

> **'Trust became a cornerstone of successful empires. Trust in Rome's coins was
> so strong that they were accepted outside of the Empire's borders.
> Indians had such confidence in it that they termed their own generic term
> for coinage denarius and, from this, the Muslim caliphs Arabised the
> word to dinars, still the official name for currency throughout the Arab world.'**
> **Yuval Noah Harari, *Sapiens***

As trading routes expanded, it became increasingly difficult to lug around large quantities of cash. Often these would have been heavy and made one vulnerable to theft. Merchants now began to use promissory notes as methods of dealing with trusted associates. It's thought that the first banknotes grew out of this, even though the idea didn't really catch on until thousands of years later when the Chinese first began to use them as 'flying money' in the 7th century AD.

Later, banks and governments were to recognise their use, but with this also came the need to guarantee the underlying value in hard bullion. This might all have seemed a good plan but, of course, it was one that was to fail enough times for peoples' fortunes to fluctuate alarmingly.

> '**Again and again throughout history, trust has to start with relatives before it can be extended to strangers. Sending relatives abroad as agents has a long history.**'
> **Matt Ridley,** *The Rational Optimist*

Today, the amount of tangible cash in the world has completely decoupled both from its bullion backing and from the real money that's in circulation. We now use what's known as 'fiat' money, imaginary money, that's so called because the early Florentine bankers used to describe it with the expression 'let it be done'.

This imbalance between real and imagined currencies may appear as a terrifying concept, but in many ways it's the ultimate statement of belief as a system of cooperation among the peoples of the world. Trust the money, in other words, and you trust in the future and in the governments that support it. But should one sleep soundly at night? Possibly not.

Interesting as all these great changes might have been throughout our history, do they really deserve to be described as revolutionary? In what ways could they be said to have changed our existence?

Well, if we accept that our entire human story has been one of overcoming the same life forces that have shaped every other organism since the emergence of the first cell, then yes, the invention of the 'brain outside the brain' has to rank high in the pantheon of forces that have made us who we are.

Why's that? Well, first, cooperation and symbiotic unions are life's way of holding back entropy. Human dealing, specialisation, exchange, reciprocity and trading are our versions of this - but being able to trust people you didn't know had always held us back. Now the external brain was an outsourced way of getting power from non-partisan, intermediary agents… and these all speeded up the energy efficiencies that come from sharing tasks and dividing labour. By doing this, breakthroughs like these gave structure and direction to how we dealt with each other, as well as becoming defence mechanisms against the bad guys trying to exploit us.

The unique human ability to slide around the Behavioural Spectrum is both the mainspring of our greatness, but also the source of our untrustworthiness. It's our very adroitness that means we can never be certain about where other people stand, and this realisation makes us uncertain about whether we can trust them… particularly if we think they could be as dodgy and self-serving as we are.

Our animal heritage makes us want to win - winning is survival - and while we always want to be trusted, our instinct to look out for Number One could be so strong that it sometimes made us shy away from being good partners. With writing, recording and money we'd now invented mechanisms for pinning people down, and by doing this, trust in strangers could finally expand. Besides anything else, these 'facts' now gave us ways of satisfying our acute human compulsion for knowing where we were in life. Like everything else, the more secure we felt, the more adventurous we could become.

Secondly, though, the external brain legitimises hierarchies. This gives it a good claim on being a revolutionary step for us. The elite classes now had ways of recording and communicating knowledge that the great majority of people didn't share, and couldn't influence. The Big Man's lust for hard evidence to ward off any accusations of parasitism was increasingly being met, because written facts were a great deal more credible for underpinning his authority than questionable myths.

As data recording took hold, the Big Men increasingly found they could formalise the pecking order, lay down codes to say how society should work, monitor what people were achieving, equate crimes to their punishments, and above all, establish a large gap between themselves as rulers - and everyone else below them.

But however much they may have tried to set in granite the relationship between those at the top and the vast bulk of people who made up the rest… any understanding between the two groups was always uneasy and fluid. And it remains so to this day. The toffs may want respect, but recorded history is very largely a narrative of our repeated attempts to find out exactly what they were doing to deserve it.

Philosophers and social commentators would have been a thorn in the side of the ruling classes all those millennia ago, every bit as they are now. And however much a monarch might have tried to prescribe how people should live together, there were always opportunities for religious geniuses to provide another kind of leadership. How did they do this? Mainly by dumbing down the rigid instructions that rulers used, and instead describing society in a way that the masses could easily understand.

Moses, for example, wasn't being elitist or hard to understand when he said that God's law could be summarised in just Ten Commandments. Similarly, Jesus was to establish the most widely followed religion on earth with just a three second instruction: 'Love God, and love your neighbour as yourself'. The idea that the complications of life could be unravelled and smoothed out by such universal statements, backed up by a few generally accepted points of guidance, were to prove to be keystones in the history of human culture.

Thirdly, however, possibly the most counter-intuitive consequence of the 'brain outside the brain' was the way that it could now multiply the effects of our human intelligence. As Robert Wright puts it in *Nonzero*: 'The revolution in agricultural technology made society more secure and more dense in numbers - the more people, the more brain.'

And it was the consequence of this wildly growing amount of shared knowledge that precipitated the avalanche of innovation, enterprise and progress for both individuals and societies that began around now. The more people knew, and the more problems became exposed… the more that human ingenuity was showing itself capable of solving them.

As ever, the engines that drove this urge to innovate were the profound linkage between the worldly triumphs that served as mate signaling, getting lots of sex and genetic fecundity. Basic forces at work? So it would seem - the better you did, the more attractive you were. Success really could breed success. But, hey, whatever works.

So what did all this add up to?

Well, it's around this period in our history that anthropologists begin to describe humans as becoming civilised. Quite what this means is hard to say. It's one of those concepts that seems to have as many definitions as there are individuals around to give an opinion.

But the consensus appears to be that it's what emerges when food security reaches a level that it allows societies to connect up the critical elements of specialised labour, writing, recording, trusted currencies, a governing hierarchy, artistic expression, monumental architecture and the acceptance of common religious beliefs.

By allowing all these things to come together, social cohesion follows. And this, in turn, leads on to the evolution of cooperation, the exposure of wrong-doers… and the foundation stones of a generally accepted definition of morality. As Charles Darwin foresaw in *The Descent Of Man*: 'As man advances in civilisation, small tribes are united into larger communities, the simplest reason would tell each individual that he ought to extend his social instincts and sympathies to all the members of the same nation, though personally unknown to him. This point being once reached, there is only an artificial barrier to prevent his sympathies extending to the men of all nations and races.' Quite so. Although one wonders when we'll truly get there.

Does this add up to a revolution? It would seem so to me… but if this is the case then, where did it lead? For one thing, Darwin seems to have been hazy about what he meant by 'sympathies'. And the history of mankind certainly continued to unfold in a blood-soaked and repressive way. In spite of this, we were clearly managing to hold onto some of the lessons and advantages of non-zero collaboration.

So, what happened next?

450 acres of prime London real estate, owned by the Duke of Westminster. He's one of the richest men in the world and a global celebrity. We're still fascinated by people like this... but why?

CHAPTER ELEVEN

WRITING AND RECORDING CERTAINLY HELPED PEOPLE OVERCOME THE TRUST BARRIER IN LARGER SOCIETIES - AND THIS LED TO FAR GREATER SCOPE FOR SPECIALISATION AND EXCHANGE. BUT IT ALSO LED TO REPRESSIVE HIERARCHIES AND STRATIFIED SOCIAL ORDERS. YES, THERE MIGHT HAVE BEEN WINNERS, BUT THERE WERE ALSO MASSES OF DOWNTRODDEN LOSERS. SO WHAT HAPPENED NEXT?

There are a few topics I've always felt it's useful to steer clear of when one's out for a nice dinner with friends. One is money. Politics is probably another. But a third might be the hypothesis that genetic evolution inevitably leads to human culture. And that our social behaviour can therefore be explained in biological terms.

This tends to be a hot subject if someone's signed up to the belief that they're linked, because its implication can only mean that we don't have the freedom to control our lives. We're not our own masters, in other words; we're simply slaves to our genetic inheritance, and powerless to alter the selfish drives that are so evident in other organisms.

The random outcomes of mutations, the quite separate motivations of genes and their vehicles, the unknown effects of environmental change, the distinction between competitive and cooperative drives, the unimaginable timescales, the critical difference between Darwin's exhortation to 'let' natural selection take place rather than to force it, and above all a recognition that *human behaviour may be shaped by our genes but that we also have the capacity to reject their instructions…* can all somehow manage to get lost in the flinging down of napkins and a torrent of hissed mutters like: 'I suppose you think Hitler had a point! In your book, perhaps children with a squint should be drowned at birth?'

At moments like this one feels there's probably a good living to be had for someone dressed up as Herbert Spencer to be summoned by the covert pressing of a mobile app and directed by a GPS location system, who'd then stroll up and gracefully explain what he actually meant by 'survival of the fittest'.

'Darwin did not say that mental powers would inevitably be explained by appeal to natural selection. Instead, he made a bet that mental powers in humans and other animals would be explained by an appeal to gradual historical processes.'

Tim Lewens, *Cultural Evolution*

As it happens, most academic theorists seem to be OK with the idea that our cultural development shares a number of fundamental similarities with the gene based theory of evolution.

But where many of these same people can blow a fuse, however, is when they begin to conflate the things they can see on the surface of the ocean of life, like the waves made up of phenotypic effects and behavioural decisions, with the deeper currents of directional forces that caused these waves to happen in the first place. Certainly any attempt to draw up laws of human history that are based on these vectors have always provoked a mixed reception. In fact, they can often make for troubled waters.

These views were particularly deepened when Bill Hamilton's explanation of how the role of altruism was the seminal factor in the development of 'selfish' gene theory first appeared. But by the mid 1970s many theorists were now taking this concept even further, and a number of high-profile academics were now publishing books that explained the biological logic behind our genetic backgrounds.

Much of the focus in these was on examining the mechanisms employed by eusocial insects, and the importance of their gene-driven self-sacrifices. But the problem of these strategies was that it was also a short step from there for people to imagine their flip side, and to concentrate instead on the brutal, parasitic and predatory behaviours that were other aspects of the decision-making process.

But did this necessarily mean that *Homo sapiens* was also following these behavioural strategies? After all, people were asking, if our evolutionary descent mirrored that of every other organism, then what was stopping us from having these same aspects to our natures? Logic might suggest that we did, but for many people these implications were extremely concerning. And when they first appeared, protests began to break out against the idea.

This was particularly so in the US where objectors frequently worked themselves up into a fury at the principle, and sometimes jumped a few too many hoops to arrive at the conclusion that mild-mannered naturalists were veering into explanations of human behaviour that were based on unpleasant zero sum drives like Hamiltonian Spite.

Many thought that these theorists were saying that people did terrible things - had become Nazis for example - because they'd been ordered to by their genetic inheritance. So, did we have free will, intellect, reasoning and morals, went the accusing questions? Or was our culture just a lick of paint that covered up 'the law of the jungle'? And that the violence of our hunter-gatherer ancestors was due to our animalistic lust for power hierarchies?

To what extent did our genes predetermine our behaviour was the main question. And could the answer to this imply that some people were genetically superior to others, that racial differences were understandable, and that eugenics were permissible? Rampaging rows about things like this were now going far beyond dinner table disagreements, and it wasn't long before a few of the loonier brigade were accusing high-profile biologists of goose-stepping their way through the campuses of Princeton and Stamford, shouting out deranged rationales for genocide.

One of the leading figures that was seen as standing in front of the tanks of Nature as they rolled towards the quivering innocents of culture was a well-known Harvard academic called Stephen Jay Gould, a hero of the Left and the leading 'jerk' of evolutionary theory.

Gould was the person who was probably most responsible for proposing that long periods of stasis in the history of life on earth were punctuated by short explosions of rapid change. These sudden jumps forward, he said, were the result of biological or behavioural accidents, even random shifts in the climate. When they happened, his conclusion was that the natural selection process then went barmy, and that this led species to have sudden blooms before the evolutionary process would slow, and then settle down for the changes to consolidate.

'Humans are animals and everything we do lies within our biological potential.
The statement that humans are animals does not imply that our specific
patterns of behaviour and social arrangements are in any way directly determined
by our genes. Potentiality and determination are different concepts.'
Stephen Jay Gould: *Biological Potentiality vs. Biological Determinism*

Gould had long been a sparring partner of Richard 'Selfish Gene' Dawkins, on the issue of the degree to which our genes were responsible for our actions. In addition to this, though, the two were also banging heads on the importance that Dawkins believed 'memes' played in our cultural evolution. These units of information, he claimed, were critical to the way we'd developed as a species, and that they'd taken on an ever *greater* influence as human culture had become more complex with the invention of language, social structures, myths and a belief in moral standards.

His conviction was that memes behaved like genes as they spread through societies, and that this led to their effects mushrooming as new cultural stimuli were introduced. The introduction of writing and recorded data, as an example, meant that people would have had more homogeneous outlooks because breakthroughs like these led to similar messages being memetically absorbed.

For these reasons, he and other evolutionary theorists were now talking about human development as being driven by 'dual inheritance theory', in which both genes and memes had similarly powerful influences. The implication was that we weren't simply being instructed on what to do by our genes in the way other organisms were (or people feared), but that we were profoundly shaped by our capacity to imitate the behaviour of others - and particularly the more successful individuals among us.

Professor Dawkins argued that these memes could also be labelled 'selfish', because they might find themselves at odds with what one's genes were instructing. Deciding on whether we should reproduce, cooperate, or destroy others, for instance, are among the most obvious examples of this.

With the 'brain outside the brain' of shared information now becoming increasingly widespread, the human race was changing faster than at any point in our history. It was apparent that the more ways there were of memes being delivered, then the more impact they were having when they reached people's heads. And if the messages we were receiving were all saying the same thing, then we'd end up assuming that our cultural beliefs were the *natural* reasons for the way societies worked.

The external brain was increasingly catalysing this process as recorded 'facts' rammed imaginary constructs into people's heads. And this meant that instead of us wondering if certain types had the right to rule us, or whether intricate religious beliefs were actually credible, we were all largely buying into the same ideas. Of course there wasn't much scope for doing anything other than this, because this was how societies worked, and the Big Man's military clout ensured that people stayed in line. Taken together, all these sources of power were now combining to form a mutually supporting ruling class that sat at the top of the stratified hierarchies of larger societies.

The control the gang at the top exerted was absolute. One might almost say that its members - the ruling dynasties, priests, cronies, high castes, landowners, nobles, generals and so on - were all joined together into a parasitical protection racket that sat on the back of everyone who wasn't in the cosy club. It became a conspiracy of interests, micromanaging the lives of non-members, and insisting on what they should do and think. At the same time it was constantly telling them that they should be grateful for being governed in this way.

There were also features of our non-sentient backgrounds that were adding to this state of affairs. The underlying power of kin selection, for example, meant that authoritarian forces automatically favoured their relations over outsiders. Altruism within families stems from genetic connections, and this was now feeding into selective behaviour.

The gene lines of the elite class were therefore being extended by nepotism, and this was then being reinforced by education and a stacked justice system. Add these all up, and as the size of communities grew, a collective assumption took hold that these sorts of superior people had no need to labour for their living. Over time this was baked ever deeper into our group neuropsychology.

It's hardly surprising, therefore, that as the creation myths, invented rules and reputational legends were pumped out and came to dominate the lives of the lower orders, it was only very rarely that the underdogs ever seemed to lift their heads and say: 'hang on a minute, why am I doing all the work and you lot are swanning around making my life so difficult? Why do I have to put up with all your laws, regulations and restrictions?'

Rather more to the point, why didn't the have-nots become more fed up with the deal they were getting? In fact, why didn't they rebel more often than they did?

Perhaps it was here, possibly more than anywhere else, that our common genetic background was making us conform to the directions of travel of the natural world. This was because the underclass in these societies were acting out exactly the same symbiotic relationships that appear among other organisms - but in their case it was between themselves and the bosses. And even though their numbers were so great that they might represent 95% or more of the population, the great majority of people didn't reject their rulers… because they were getting just enough out of the deal to make the arrangement acceptable.

Just as in Nature, arrangements like this obviously work, however unbalanced they might appear from the outside. One partner may seem to be getting more out of the arrangement than the other, but if there are adequate benefits for them both - then the outcome of the union ends up suiting each of them. When this happens, the result is a long-lasting (although never entirely relaxed) relationship - even though the constant changes that inevitably come along will eventually threaten it.

In exactly this way, the profound forces that had led to the settled societies of around 3,000 BCE were now acting in a similar way to the ones that had shaped our genetic evolution. Just as we'd developed from organisms like sponges and slime moulds in which the cells had all carried out the same functions, we'd then evolved to become complex entities that relied on the interaction of hundreds of specialised cells.

Now, in a startlingly similar progression, social Darwinism was taking us away from the simplicity and uniformity of hunter-gatherer groups, and towards the explosion of crafts, skills, professions, shared data, specialisation and exchange and interlocking benefits that the growing cities now encouraged.

'At some basic level, cultural evolution and biological evolution have the same machinery. Second, they have the same fuel: the energetic interplay between zero sum and non-zero sum forces has been similarly pervasive in the two evolutions. Third, the two processes have parallel directions - long-run growth in non-zero sumness, and thus in the depth and scope of complexity.'

Robert Wright, *Nonzero*

'I just don't think there are equal
benefits in this social symbiosis.'

The Secrets of Life - Book Two

All good you'd think (surely the more complex we are, the greater the energy efficiencies must be?) but the quid pro quo that people now demanded was to have social mechanisms in place that protected them from the balance of the symbiosis getting upset. Yes, they'd accept the toffs and their suppression strategies, the majority now seemed to be saying, but the deal had to be balanced with safeguards against unscrupulous takers like the cheats, thieves, counterfeiters and dangerous types that took advantage of their efforts and trust.

In other words, the masses wanted protection. Critically, they wanted property rights. And who was going to provide the protection? Ha, the very people who were exploiting them in the first place - the layers of presumptuous and self-regarding autocrats at the top of the command and control pyramid that ran everything.

This arrangement plainly worked pretty well for the people who'd grabbed their top dog places early, and who had then set about brainwashing everyone else that they'd been naturally selected, even divinely chosen. But as with the failures of organisms in Nature to ever find a truly evolutionarily stable state, every cultural construct was bound to have its weaknesses too. The consequence of all this was that the rulers of the emerging states were now going to have to grapple with three great problems… and, in many ways, they've continued to struggle with them ever since.

First, it was inevitable that Big Men would become inflexible in their views, and stick too rigidly to the methods they'd always used to rule by.

They'd have had to do this because once they'd set themselves up to be omnipotent, then they had to be right all the time. This meant that these early kings and their supporters would have found it hard to adapt to innovations, or to change, or progress of any kind, even though these were all essential things if they'd wanted to build robust societies that were open to new ideas. However, if they'd allowed other ways of doing things, then this could only mean that they hadn't been right in the first place - something that was obviously impossible if they wanted remain credible as an absolute monarch.

Secondly, members of the farming class that had helped develop successful city states were increasingly evolving into large-scale landowners. As they did this they were becoming too important to be ignored by the elites, even if they didn't let them sit at the top table. What to do about them? Easy - absorb them into the ruling architecture.

This was either done by simply grabbing their land by force, or more usually by marriage, and then making the land holdings part of the power base. Simmer the system for a few thousand years and you end up with a country that's actually *owned* by the Big Men. And with this would come a repressed work force that had become dependent on agricultural work, who lived in virtual slavery, had scant rights even though they made up the majority of the population, and who were generally cowed by the threat of starvation. The result was serfdom and the feudal system.

Even today - even after all the upheaval of modern wars and the progress that social justice has made for land ownership to become more egalitarian - it remains deep in the belief systems of settled societies that a nation's very *soil* represents the ultimate wealth. Naturally, this is less true for countries that have regularly suffered from invasion, where its people generally prefer to have valuable things they can pick up and carry away.

But it was the third weakness that was to have the greatest effect on how societies developed. What happened was that the top-down models of government systems were increasingly being forced to recognise that the masses wanted trustworthy structures that allowed them to trade freely with each other.

Among other things, they expected rulers to respect their basic rights to have specialised skills and acknowledged places in society. Governments, they were saying, should provide a level playing field that ensured people weren't constantly at risk of exploitation. Not too much to ask, was it? Yet this simple request was to be the backdrop for most of the conflicts of human history.

There was also another aspect to this need, however, because the growing scale and prosperity of societies was seeing the emergence of a different type of operator. And these were people who understood the need for protection, even if the elites would rather bury their heads in the sand than deal with it..

This new bunch were smart cookies who'd become talented at the buying and selling processes that reliable money had unleashed. And they were now pushing themselves forward to provide the lubricants so necessary to make society's non-zero machine hum. What they understood was that the supply and demand process meant they'd have to buy in bulk... and this encouraged the best producers. And, just as importantly, they also recognised that problems could be solved with innovation and invention - and they had the money to bring new things to market.

These people were merchants, and they'd begun developing into a powerful force in society, largely because they made their livings by investing in the *future* in a way that the ruling class could never understand. Monarchs snatched at things, arrogant about their rights. But they were also desperate for money to keep their layers of nobility happy.

Merchants did the opposite: they held stock and took a profit as things passed through them. They were the opposite of the kings, priests and generals with their zero sum outlooks and constant anxieties about being overthrown. Instead, this new trading class appreciated that they needed to deal with the common man, and they understood why it was necessary to generate win/win outcomes.

They could also see the repression that came with being ruled by a hierarchy. They weren't interested in it, however, because they realised that the bottom-up process of trading didn't want or need a pecking order. Quite the reverse in fact: traders wanted to create networks of cooperative people.

Before long the two philosophies were colliding, and the influence of the merchant class was leading to tensions within the increasingly complex societies. Top-down authority was now having to find ways of getting along with bottom-up trading. Each needed the other, even if they had completely different aims.

'(Trade) is not a zero sum game. The simple idea of the gains from
trade lies at the heart of the modern and the ancient economy.'
Matt Ridley, *The Origins of Virtue*

Seen from their viewpoint, rulers wanted power and status without the need to do the unpleasant slog. And to achieve this they'd come to depend on cultural memes that reinforced their right a privileged life.

The merchants and the vast bulk of their customers, however, had the simpler ambition of wanting to get through life as best they could and, wherever possible, to make a little money. One force was vertically stratified downwards, while the other one came up to meet it. Zero sum presumptions were banging into non-zero cooperation. These were human versions to the natural world's responses to the 1st and 2nd Laws… but had they ever been in such conflict before?

So how did the two groups manage to get along? Surely the rising wealth of the merchants would prove to be too great a threat to the fictive aura of the Big Men? Even if they had tough guys around them who'd enforce their authority?

This was where the beneficial symbiosis between the two sides now emerged at its most obvious. The nobility might have found money a grubby concept… but because they were parasitic on society, they needed the taxes, levies, tariffs, fines and every other stunt they could pull to squeeze funds out of the trading process. Merchants, in other words, were doing their work for them, and providing the funds they so obviously needed.

In many ways, this outcome was also protecting the Big Man because whenever those in power tried to control the process of wealth generation, they inevitably ended up restricting it. Why was that? It was because they were pathologically incapable of ever appreciating the need to understand another man's thought processes. To do this would have required a desire to think like a little man, and to empathise with his needs… and these were exactly the kind of things a self-regarding Big Man was incapable of doing.

Instead of this, his mindset was invariably hierarchical, and because he would see himself as superior to the common man, he'd never have been able to understand the idea of letting other people think they could benefit from him. Big Men weren't interested in ever incentivising the lower layers. Their presumption made them symbols of fear, and rather than trading sensitively with their subjects, they preferred to keep a grip on them through debt, slavery, restrictions and other slap-downs like that.

Merchants, for their part, might have seemed to Big Men to be a dangerous new element in societies, particularly as they didn't have their invented origins, but it suited them to pay the protection money (sorry, taxes) to have the property rights, regulations and guaranteed currencies that meant they could trade within a trusted legal system. Immanuel Kant described the relationship between the ruling class's wish to have nothing to do with the grisly business of trade, and yet their constant need for the money it generated, as 'unsocial sociability'. He said that it: '… drives man by means of the mania for honour, domination or property to seek status among his fellows - who he cannot stand - but also cannot stand to *leave alone*.'

By 2,000 BCE, these forces were being felt alongside the development of ever larger communities, varied craft skills, and the way we were controlling our surroundings. Put together, these were all saying that we were very definitely no longer just another kind of animal. Instead, we'd become the most dominant species on earth. Population sizes continued to grow, and the number of domesticated animals being bred would by now have exceeded those in the wild. We humans were sitting at the apex of our environments, and the things in them, in a way that no organism had ever managed before.

Two memes had by this time completely established themselves in us. The first was that we'd become completely sold on the idea of hierarchies, something you still see in today's sophisticated societies, never mind then. Modern man might have rebelled so utterly against the influence of our genes that we can question every demand they make, but we remain so respectful of the pecking order that it almost seems to defy logic. Don't believe me? Then just look at the way we still press our noses up against the glass of politics, royalty, sporting heroes, celebrities and so on, fascinated by the intimate details of the lives of these winners, and of how our 'superior' brethren live.

The second thing that had become a common belief was the total rejection of the way people had lived in the past. Up until this point we'd always limited our group sizes and expansion ambitions but now, as yields and populations boomed in scale, we became addicted to the idea of *growth*.

Just as non-zero relationships in the natural world lead to efficiencies, so the expansion of trading was leading to greater gains and, from there, to greater opportunities. And this was a self-generating machine, because as agriculture and wealth creation fed ever larger numbers, more people equated to more brain power, from there to more exposure of the problems, to more innovation, to more consumers, and to more opportunities.

We fell in love with growth. Not only did the bottom-up process bring its own momentum, but the pressure coming down in the opposite direction was leading the elites to expand their presence too. Rulers, and the type of people that have always surrounded them, became larger and ever more greedy as the scale of communities leapt. Inevitably, this led them to dream up more and more magnificent displays of power, and to commission vast vanity projects that confirmed their credibility. What a time it must have been to be an architect.

It was also around this point in human history that one of the great truths of our genetic inheritance came into play. This was the interpretation that David Sloan Wilson summed up so clearly in his extraordinary book, *Does Altruism Exist?* when he wrote: 'We are evolution's latest major transmission. Alone among primate species, we crossed the threshold from groups *of* organisms to groups *as* organisms.'

We began, in other words, to see the individual parts of our societies as coming together and mimicking the function of a living thing - with all its different specialised parts - and its own controlling brain. It must have been around now that we began to develop a group mind that, at a deep and only mistily understood level, seemed to know where it wanted society to go.

Sloan Wilson goes on to argue that, as this new organism became increasingly sophisticated: 'Our ancestors managed to suppress disruptive forms of within-group competition, making benign forms of within-group selection and between-group selection the primary evolutionary forces.'

What does this mean? Well, he's saying that the more we were evolving to cooperate within the group - the organism that is society - the more competitive we become against *other* groups. We still see this everywhere around us. Even in something like football, the better the team, the more organised it is, the higher their skills, the more that individuals play for each other, the less they hog the ball, and the higher their team spirit is… the more likely it is that they'll win the league.

I'm sure Sloan Wilson would never have been so casual in the way he'd have expressed this as I have. But even he boils everything down to a single conclusion to the meta-studies that he and EO Wilson conducted into the behaviour of all life forms. In particular, that of eusocial insects.

By labelling the behaviour behind the forces at work as either *selfish* (in that they increase relative fitness within groups) or *altruistic* (when they increase the fitness of the group but this places the individual at a relative fitness disadvantage) these two great evolutionary theorists collaborated to come up with their famous one-line insight into the whole subject: 'Selfishness', they asserted, 'beats altruism within groups. But altruistic groups beat selfish groups.'

Has this pivotal interpretation of the natural world any significance for us humans? It sure does. Indeed, if one looks at the sweep of our history, it's evident that selfishness had been the winning strategy in the making of these larger communities. The definition of the governing classes was that they were entirely looking out for themselves, taking as much as they could and letting the mass of people get as little as possible.

But because human societies are like every other organism in needing to get their energy from somewhere, if we wanted more of it for growth, then it meant that the easiest way of doing this was to get everyone to collaborate… and take it from somewhere else.

And so, (and look away now if you don't want to hear the implication of all this), what the drumbeat of our genes were pounding out when they were working in tandem with our cultural evolution, was that the more organised our societies became, and the more convinced a group was that it was superior to its neighbours, the more motivated it became to rub them out.

We now know what lies behind this. In the natural world, colonies of eusocial insects illustrate that self-sacrificing strategies like sterility, or things like the selflessness of a death-inducing sting, were genetically worthwhile for a community's defence. In other words, altruistic, within-group behaviour was immensely productive.

But now we humans came up with a twist on this evolutionary tactic that was to take it a step further. We discovered a cooperative strategy that would see everyone in society work together to satisfy both the ambitions of the top-down forces, and yet grow the opportunities for the bottom-up process as well. What was the upshot?

We invented aggressive warfare.

'War?', you're probably asking, no doubt with an appalled look coming over your fine features. 'What good has ever come from that?'

'Last chance. Take back what you said about my wife!'
(War wasn't always as serious as this.)

CHAPTER TWELVE

AGGRESSIVE WARFARE? HOW COULD ANYTHING SO DESTRUCTIVE AND NIHILISTIC HAVE EVER CONTRIBUTED TO HUMAN PROGRESS? SURELY IT WOULD HAVE STOPPED NON-ZERO ACTIVITIES IN THEIR TRACKS? WHAT POSSIBLE BENEFITS COULD EVER EMERGE FROM IT?

Violent conflict? That's a horrible conclusion. How could wars have possibly boosted an emerging civilisation, let alone suited the governing class that controlled it? And never mind them - what about the poor citizens who were trying to better themselves?

Well, the awful truth was that picking a fight with another culture turned out to be a highly profitable strategy… just as long as you could beat your opponent. A monarch's mindset was always zero sum, and if he won by crushing his enemy's armies then it was high fives all round.

First, he could give the loser's cultivated land to his cronies and generals to keep them quiet.

Secondly, he could then smash the other side's temples and their religious beliefs, annihilate their menfolk, use their women as breeding machines (victors always had multiple wives), spread his own people's genes wider, and generally impose his cultural memes onto a whole load of new people.

Not only did this mean that his religion was the right one, and that his gods had clearly picked the winner, but it also led his culture's system of government to tighten around even larger numbers of suppressed people. This all added up to the Big Man's legitimacy being wildly enhanced.

Instead of having to rely on myths about his origins, or right to rule, he was now the man who'd defeated the Medes, the Assyrians, the Shang (or whichever other unfortunate race had been brought to its knees). There was obviously nothing *invented* about that.

The result? More glory, more power, more credibility… and more *income*. On the face of it, this kind of greatness grab was a no brainer.

It's a logic that we still see today. In my own world, a Chief Executive that's run out of ideas for organic growth frequently turns his sights on acquisitions. The argument he puts to his shareholders is always along the lines of … 'we'll cut out a lot of their workforce, and our central office can then run the merged operation. That way, everything will drop to the bottom line and the profit's bound to be enhanced.' (Ha, if only, seems to be the lesson of commercial history.)

But what of the common man in all this theorising? What of the people who would have done more than their fair share of the fighting and dying? Well, who cares about them seems to have been the prevailing attitude of the Big Man - couldn't they see that he had to be right? No doubt he'd already have whipped them up into a passionate hatred of their neighbours, and everyone likes to squash their enemies, don't they?

As for the merchant class, they'd have been delighted by the outcome. Of course their side had to win, but if it did then they'd have been cracking out the champagne. Why's that, because you'd think that having places wrecked and their populations impoverished would be bad for business? Yet it turns out that the opposite is true. Wars have always been economically expansionist for a number of reasons.

First, because your own people have to cooperate to be an effective conquering force, the collective energy of their non-zero activities would have turbocharged productivity.

Secondly, armies needed weapons, clothing, provisions and payment - all things that created an economic stimulus. Innovative products would have come through as well, generally at a far faster pace than usual. There was now an urgent need for them.

And last, perhaps most importantly, if things worked out and merchants had invested in the winner, they'd find that they could enormously increase their trading range. Markets would now be bigger, the defeated country probably needed rebuilding, its crushed and cowering populace would be using the victor's language and customs, and your legal system and standards of good practice would now be theirs as well.

The winner's currency and conditions of business would have to be accepted, and the defeated population would now be doing things a new way. Not only that, but they'd be desperate for whatever the merchants that came with the conquering army could provide, because their own traders would either have been slaughtered or come under the winning side's instructions.

Chaos was bound to reign for a bit, but at this stage money was the trust system that overcame any cultural divide… and, once the dust had settled, even old enemies would hunker down to cooperate through specialisation and exchange. Instead of continuing to be hostile, everyone would now be facing the same way, and the trading opportunities would inevitably expand.

So, yes, undoubtedly these ancient societies would have found wars were brutal and pitiless affairs, but they were also discovering how cultural unification could follow.

The conclusion was inescapable: large-scale conflicts were one of the most powerful catalysts for the growth of non-zero activity. In spite of the bloodshed and misery, the destruction and the smashed beliefs, the most ironic of the outcomes of warfare was that money and trust and collaboration would *grow*. Perhaps even more paradoxically, the horrible truth was that the greed and selfishness of the Big Man's instincts would end up serving the public interest.

Robert Wright makes very much the same points in *Nonzero*. Looked at over the millennia, he says, war has been part of the trend towards consolidation and higher levels of political organisation. In short, mass conflicts may be zero sum, but they generate non-zero cooperation. And from all this come the conditions that inevitably lead to a fast track expansion in cultural evolution.

The anthropologist and historian Ian Morris takes a similarly long view in his book *War! What Is It Good For?*

In this he makes the point that while violence and aggressive warfare seem to have been a uniquely human curse - and that the pattern of our development may act in a frustratingly zigzag manner - the underlying trend has always been towards a reduction in war deaths. This is because, he says: '… by fighting wars, people have created larger, more organised societies that have reduced the risk that their members will die violently.'

However much we may instinctively disagree, research shows that the so-called pastoral paradise of hunter-gatherers was a delusion. In fact, their territorial paranoia led to primitive people having as much as a 20% chance of dying at the hands of another person. Compared to this, even throughout the blood-soaked horrors of the twentieth century, the average world citizen would actually have had no more than a 1-2% likelihood of a similar death.

But, of course, the Big Men of the Ancient World quickly discovered they had to *win* to make the idea work. Many a ruler would have felt the hot breath of his people when he was whipping them up for a fight, but he could easily overplay his hand by choosing the wrong lot to go to war with. He might not like to think about it… but he could lose.

> **'Wars happen because the ones who start them think they can win.'**
> **Margaret Atwood, *Morning in the Burned House***

This kind of error was truly zero sum - from hero to zero in one step. They must have realised it too, and sometimes they'd have hesitated with good reason. When Philip of Macedonia was threatening to invade Laconia, for instance, he sent a message to its city-state of Sparta.

'You are advised to submit without further delay', he wrote, 'for if I bring my army into your land, I will destroy your farms, slay your people, and raze your city.'

The Laconians replied with the bluntness and brevity that would later give the world the description 'laconic':

'If.'

Nothing more needed to be said. And neither Philip nor his son, Alexander the Great, ever tried it on with them again.

> **'To win one hundred victories in one hundred battles is not the acme**
> **of skill. To subdue the enemy without fighting is the acme of skill.'**
> **Sun Tzu, *The Art of War***

Even so, what were the implications of all this logic?

Perhaps highest on the list of conclusions was that any aggressor had to avoid inciting warfare that could tip over from zero sum to becoming negative sum. This was a state of affairs that could make *both* sides worse off. Robert Wright highlights the impact of this in *Nonzero*, when he says that the prevailing fear was that these kinds of low technology conflicts could drag on, and that this made the decision to wage war less about aggression… and more about *waging peace*.

> 'By fighting wars, people have created larger, more organised
> societies that have reduced the risk that their members will die violently.'
> Ian Morris, *'War! What Is It For?'*

To underpin the same view, Wright goes on to describe the summary the anthropologist Elman Service proposes in *Origins of the State and Civilisation*: ' … war is just another reason to value the harmony that comes from economic integration; it isn't to fight wars that society evolves, so much as to escape wars, to carve out broader and sturdier war-free zones.'

How did these war-free zones evolve? Well, they emerged around the same time as the invention of writing and recording because it was about then that the Big Men would have stumbled on a system of governance that was to make such good sense that it's been in place pretty much unchanged ever since. That system was… *empire*.

Did it work? Yes, beautifully, because if an enemy could be flattened, the strength of the winning empire's central command system allowed it to govern different territories and cultures without having to change its own character or structure.

As time passed, this concept began to evolve into ever more flexible systems with things like civilising missions, *lingua franca* and the passing on of the conqueror's societal values. Eventually other cultures would come to admire and copy these… whether they liked it or not. But, in the early days, the model depended solely on conquest. Just the iron fist was the first stage strategy - and to hell with the velvet glove.

The idea first took off when King Narmer used force of arms to combine the Upper and Lower valleys of Egypt to form the Old Kingdom. Further east, a few centuries later, the Akkadian Empire was established around 2,300 BCE and created a huge Mesopotamian union that was to last through eight reigns and 180 years.

Yet the Akkadians pale into insignificance when they're compared to the Assyrian Empire that succeeded it. This behemoth managed to combine the vast regions of modern day Iraq, Turkey, Iran and Syria and kept evolving so that it continued to exist, in one form or another, for nearly fifteen hundred years. It was said at the time to cover the 'Four Corners of the World'.

Alongside this, in the ancient world, were the Babylonians, the Hittites, the Egyptians and the Nubians, each adopting a similar model of crush and absorb. Not terribly subtle but highly effective for all that - and all of them would have led to economic growth. In the Far East the empires of the Shang, and later the Zhou, had even greater landmasses under their control. Both of them then splintered and weren't unified again for a further five hundred years.

Around 600 BCE there was then a cultural lurch towards ever-greater magnificence and splendour. The so-called Axial Age of the first millennium saw the glories of the Achaemenid, or Persian, empire last for 220 years as various emperors followed Cyrus the Great in dominating gigantic landholdings. This was a great success on one level with its homogeneous prescription for governance, centralised bureaucracy, official languages, infrastructure projects and general magnificence, yet its weakness was that, fatally, it never managed to get over a shared vision of national identity.

Eventually it was threatened by Philip of Macedonia's mixture of wild threats and bribery. His aim had always been to bring down the Persian emperors, but he was assassinated before he could achieve it. There was then a pause before his son, Alexander, completed the mission. Success over the old enemy gave Alexander an enduring taste for the rough stuff, and he went on to open up a colossal swathe of territory into one continuous Hellenistic empire that arced for thousands of miles from Egypt in the west, right the way across to India.

Alexander was possibly one of the few to combine the divine with the sword. He was conceived, went the mythology, when his mother's womb was struck by a lightning bolt with the result that he managed, somehow, to be a son not only to Philip, but also to both Zeus and the Egyptian god of the air, Amun. Remarkably he also claimed a seamless lineage that went back to Achilles and Heracles.

Tutored as a child by Aristotle, he combined the forces of the Greek city-states into a federation after his father's death, and then ran a number of different conquest and governance models to create his empire. These ranged from handing out appalling levels of slaughter to a region if it dared to resist, through to leaving some cultures and religions almost intact if their leaders capitulated.

Once he'd destroyed the Persians, for example, he forced his (rather grumpy) military leaders into a cultural merger with the old order by arranging a mass marriage with the widows of the rulers he'd had killed. No doubt they'd have been even grumpier. Perhaps more extraordinary was the way that he conquered Egypt in 332 BC, and yet was so dazzled by the richness of its culture that he decreed that nothing should be changed, and that its beliefs could remain intact.

Even by the bloody standards of the Ancient World, nobody had ever seen a rampage like Alexander's. He conquered over two million square miles in thirteen years, founded seventy cities in his own name and even one in memory of his horse. He was said to have wept for the want of worlds to conquer. And, by the age of thirty-three, he was dead.

The Axial Age also saw the spread of new ideas and religions that were themselves influential in shaping global cultures, as much then as now. The Zoroastrians of Persia were among the most important of these, imagining a single god and devil battling it out for dominance. This was a concept that was to then hold sway over many religions as they repeatedly saw life as a binary choice between the forces of good and evil, light and dark.

The Fab Four... all alive at the same time.

Humanist religions also began springing up in a number of different places. In another of those extraordinary cases of 'ideas whose time had come', four separate humanist approaches were founded within a few years of each other. Astonishingly, this meant that the Buddha, the Jain Mahavira, Confucius and Lao Tzu were all alive at the same time.

The Chinese were particularly influenced by Confucianism in their approach to structuring their empires. The Han, for example, may have retained much of the Qin imperial bureaucracy, but their emperors reduced the harsher aspects of the previous system, and encouraged greater moral virtues in place of rules based solely on fear and repression.

Similarly, Southeast Asian empires would later incorporate a Buddhist mindset into their seaborne empires. These reached out from the mainland to the countless islands of Indonesia and Malaysia.

The Khmer empire went even further by welding Hinduism onto their core Buddhist beliefs, and ruled from their great centre at Angkor until they, too, subsided after roughly 600 years. The Siamese and other neighbouring empires then continued for a further five centuries.

Back in the ancient world, the rise of the Phoenicians saw the birth of a North African empire that stretched in a great sweep across the top of the continent, through the 'shining city' of Carthage, and ruling over three hundred far-flung cities with an influence that was to extend into large parts of the Iberian peninsula.

In spite of being almost constantly in conflict with both the Roman Empire and the Greeks in Sicily, the Carthaginians had learnt that the military model didn't come without its problems. They'd looked at how other empires did things and concluded that direct control of one's conquered territories was expensive and tough to maintain. This was largely due to the need for distant garrisons that were engaged in endless skirmishes - and it didn't come cheap. Bigger operations needed yet more regulation and, with the repression this unleashed, there'd be further threats of ever more serious uprisings.

Instead, Carthage was more interested in being a central trading hub, and their governance model tended to rely more on mercenary muscle than its own people. This was a novel twist to the old models, but it turned out to have its own shortcomings. All might have gone well until the Carthaginians discovered that a bunch of hired soldiers could lose their enthusiasm for fighting to the last man when there was the real prospect of not being paid - or of dying.

Over a period of about fifty years during the second century BCE, the Carthaginians' Roman rivals across the Mediterranean fought them for regional dominance in a series of Punic Wars. The Third of these ended with a decisive victory for Rome, and was followed by its unpleasant practice of 'ploughing the lands with salt' - a tactic designed to completely destroy any prospect of an enemy's recovery.

The rest of the landholding was then added to its own, and the Roman empire would eventually extend its total reach as far as Spain in the west, and over to Constantinople in the east… before the inevitable decline set in, and its cohesion was weakened by the constant blows of the Ottomans.

> 'To ravage, to slaughter, to usurp under false title, they call
> empire; and where they make a desert, they call it peace.'
> Tacitus, *The Histories*

By now the penny was dropping that while empires might be expansive cultural unifiers, with their growing economies and shared languages and customs, they were just as prone as any other organism to competitive threats or sudden changes to their environments. As with everything in the natural world, survival would only come with evolution.

The essential problem for these early civilisations was that there were always conflicts between the two groups of people that they were supposed to be benefitting. The little man, the bottom-uppers, wanted peace and a few demands to be met such as the rule of law, protection from oppression, fair markets and the warm glow of patriotic pride. This last point was critical, and to fix it most governing elites realised pretty quickly how important it was to make their downtrodden citizens think they were on the winning side. This meant assuring them that they were being ruled by the most glorious leaders, and that the moral certainties they espoused were coming from the empire's religious beliefs.

On the other hand, the rulers, the top-downers, had other aims altogether. Their wish list would have been headed by self-centred things like growth, greater power, increased credibility and no end of glory. Oh, and a load of completely loyal subjects who weren't going to ask nasty questions or cause trouble.

Now, needless to say, the ambitions of these two different groups didn't always go together. Each side was continuously weighing up its position in a kind of instinctive cost-benefit analysis. The lower-order people could usually be kept quiet with threats and force - even though suppression was bad for consumption.

More problematic, however, was when they became less compliant, and tipped from accepting their inferior role in the social symbiosis, to getting uppity and wanting a bigger share. Sometimes the threat simply became too great to be ignored, and the

Big Men would have to pacify them with hand-outs, large-scale entertainments, or even by having a few privileges tossed in to keep them quiet.

The problem was that these little treats would come from what the ruling class thought should rightly be in their own pockets. And this was bound to make them resentful and less inclined to be so pleasant in the future.

'One of the effects of power, myriad studies show, is that it makes you see others in a negative light. If you're powerful you're more likely to think most people are lazy and unreliable. They need to be supervised and monitored, managed and regulated, censored and told what to do. And because power makes you feel superior to other people, you'll believe that all this monitoring should be entrusted to you.
Rutger Bregman, *Humankind*

The other constant irritation for the Big Man - more like a nagging anxiety actually - was that there were always challenges coming along from people who thought they had a better political model, or a more legitimate right to rule. The end result was that there was never such a thing as an evolutionary stable strategy for kings. They were never really secure, and this was particularly true at a time when their kind could be made and unmade through sudden violence. This resulted in, as Shakespeare put it in *Henry IV*: 'And in the calmest and most stillest nights... Uneasy lies the head that wears the crown.'

Rather more insistent than the threat of insurrection was that the merchant class was becoming ever stronger. And they were only too capable of sudden shifts in their loyalty if they thought the rulers were taking too much.

Empires therefore began to evolve. By the time the Romans started to move outside the Italian peninsula in the 3rd century BCE, for instance, there'd been a growing realisation that a conqueror might have to do more than simply take slaves and assume that everything that wasn't nailed down was theirs.

The concept now moved on to thinking that an empire had a far better chance of holding on to power if it also offered a superior kind of civilisation in return. Among the prime requirements for this to work were for regulated markets to operate within a stable and prosperous regime - *Pax Romana* was to become the most famous example of this - and even to include the opportunity for foreigners to climb the ladder of the central command structure. For many people at the time, rising up to hit the heights of becoming a Roman citizen was the ultimate cultural ambition.

'What did the Romans ever do for us?' Well, a great deal went the unfunny answer… but only as long as things were done *their way*. 'Roman law and Roman roads' may have been the proud boast, but their rule was absolute and, as long as they were on top, they weren't interested in any new ideas, or in sharing their authority.

Who could argue with the outlook? Their system was clearly a howling success, known to all as *imperium sine fine*, an empire without end. At its peak it would have included a hundred million subjects which, at that time, was something like a quarter of the world's population. Its total land holding extended to an area even larger than Alexander's empire, with vastly different territories that ranged from the burning Sahara to the rather damper soil of Scotland.

For much of its existence, fear was the only worthwhile instrument of power in the Roman playbook. By the time Jesus came along in an obscure corner of one of its countless provinces, for example, it didn't matter that he was painting a picture of a world in which peace, love, forgiveness and trust could flourish… all very nice, but none of this was in the Rule Book.

Since the Roman perspective only allowed for one way of responding to behaviour that they hadn't prescribed or sanctioned, they'd have had to punish it. The man was plainly not following the guidelines and therefore had to be a subversive - someone who was threatening the social order, even if he seemed a fairly harmless zealot.

Roman culture was always quick to show its subjects what they thought of those who challenged its authority. And if their strange Judean subjects preferred to see this mild man die instead of Barabbas, a notorious troublemaker, then they felt justified in handing down the same death sentence, and crucifying him between two other '*lestes*', or insurrectionists. As ever, the religious leaders were in league with the governing class, and the charge against Jesus was the one that St Luke's gospel describes as 'subverting our nation'. In other words it didn't matter what he was trying to say - the man was obviously behaving like a terrorist.

The Roman model was much admired at the time, but it proved to be very difficult to reproduce. It looked deceptively easy but it wasn't.

This was because it relied on international and cultural cohesion, yet with admirable social mobility alongside it all. The system might have had strong central control mechanisms, yet it operated with inclusive policies within its provinces. There were, for instance, common languages, yet they were never imposed. And while they had a highly professional army, its soldiers were all volunteers of a regime that often tried to avoid wars.

Many imitators would fail. Competitors might incorporate a number of Rome's features, but most found it impossible to maintain the overall vision within a wide network of customs, cultures, laws and people. And without all these bits fitting together, the social order could collapse very quickly.

The history of the world is really the history of empires. Taken together, it's reckoned there have been something like seventy of them over our history. Some were purely based on conquest, some were founded on religions like the Islamic Caliphate, some were reliant on trade, others on dynasties or racial bloodlines, and some, like the British Empire, would eventually evolve to have the loosest of bonds between the different countries.

'All human cultures are, at least in part, the legacy of empires and imperial civilisations, and no academic or political surgery can cut out the imperial legacies without killing the patient.'
Yuval Harari, *Sapiens*

Like the constant attempts in *Nature* to overcome the 1st Law by taking energy from other living things, so an empire's need for growth led to endless demands of conquest, suppression and exploitation. The social symbioses that came with the strategy were at the root of both its strengths and its weaknesses. On the one hand, most realised that a certain amount of political flexibility would improve trading levels and mollify their subjects but, on the other, it was rare that the ruling class would ever become either nurturing or far seeing.

As they evolved, there was a gradual shift to more liberal policies rather than purely relying on retribution. Later empires would try to improve the symbiotic deal with ways of getting greater productivity out of it's people. There was less stick and more carrot, and the hope was always that loyal subjects would emerge who'd integrate through the benefits of shared languages, common legal systems and political ambitions. Taken overall, it largely worked - and the great majority of *H. sapiens* that have ever drawn breath would have done so within one or other of the seemingly impregnable empires.

'So widespread was slavery in the Mediterranean and the Arabic world that even today regular greetings reference human trafficking. All over Italy, when they meet, people say to each other, 'schiavo', from a Venetian dialect.

The Secrets of Life - Book Two

'Ciao', as it is more commonly spelt, does not mean 'hello'; it means 'I am your slave'.'

Peter Frankopan, *The Silk Roads: A New History of the World*

So why didn't they last? Well, some commentators would say they have, and that the American superstate is only the latest incarnation. Others, though, point to numerous instances of the central state collapsing, citizens rebelling, or its overall power being reduced when different regions demanded independence.

Sometimes they could have political or defence issues that could undermine their integrity; sometimes there'd be environmental or economic crises. These pressures led different empires to be constantly evolving their approaches, juggling the inherent hostilities in their social orders. Just as evolutionary forces shape organisms, so the demand for change would come either from outside the organisation, or from hawkish pressures within it.

An example of this occurred as the Roman Empire fell apart. The historical view is usually that barbarian tribes simply overwhelmed Rome's exhausted dream of civilisation. But more recent theories paint an altogether different, and more interesting, version of it unfolding in a quasi 'genetic' fashion.

As Bryan Ward-Perkins puts it in *The Fall of Rome: And the End of Civilisation*: 'Instead of continuing the endless struggles to keep (the Germans) out, the Romans decided to accommodate them into the empire by an ingenious and effective arrangement. The newcomers were granted a proportion of the tax revenues of the Roman state, and the right to settle within the imperial frontiers; in exchange, they ceased their attacks, and diverted their energies into upholding Roman power, of which they were now stakeholders. In effect, they became the Roman defence force.'

Once an empire's philosophical or political cohesion failed then they were at their most vulnerable. Diocletian, for instance, had previously responded to a range of threats to Rome by thinking that its colossal scale was the root problem, and that it would function better if its authority was divided between four separate emperors. Big mistake - and certainly a wrong-headed analysis. Inevitably the arrangement collapsed, and the separation precipitated a permanent split between the western empire, which continued to be ruled from Rome, and the Byzantine empire of the east, based in Constantinople.

Many of the same forces were to later press down on the great Mongol empire of Genghis Khan. After his death it underwent many changes until it finally splintered into four discrete khanates ruled over by his grandsons. From there it inevitably weakened. In another example, the Mughal Empire in India disintegrated once the last of the dynastic line ran out. There'd been precious little 'succession planning' in spite of the country's size.

When the Emperor Aurangzeb died in 1707, he had presided over a quarter of the world's people and easily its biggest economy - larger than all of Europe's GDP combined - and the dominant centre of global manufacturing. And yet India suffered such a collapse in the early 18th century that its treasures were swiftly subsumed by outsiders, and European trading interests snaffled up the bulk of its industries.

> **'In 1775 Asia accounted for 80% of the world economy.**
> **The combined economies of India and China alone represented two thirds**
> **of global production. In comparison, Europe was an economic dwarf.'**
> **Yuval Harari *Sapiens***

Over on the other side of the world, the empires of the South American continent were similarly flawed. The Brazilian empire was overthrown by internal factions - not that unusual an outcome given the temptations of ambitious cronies. The Incas and Aztecs were conquered by better equipped and insatiably greedy foreign invaders.

The lust of the European powers for colonies led some of their empires to collapse quickly while others suffered a slow death. Some left a legacy, others became hollowed out. When Voltaire said that the Holy Roman Empire was neither holy, Roman nor an empire, he might have applied a similar description to any number of the ghost cultures that were kept alive in name only... vast superstates that, in their day, would have seemed destined to stand forever.

The vital need to create energy by transferring it over from something else is what lies at the core of competition. That's what the 1st Law dictates, and grabbing it through violence is as evident in human empire-building behaviour as any 'tooth and claw' strategy might be in the natural world.

But trying to live with the drumbeat of the 2nd Law through encouraging cooperation is equally discernible. It's at the heart of all successful symbioses, whether in human societies or empires, every bit as much as it's to be seen in chemical reactions or the physical aspects of life.

Woody Allen was right, the 2nd Law will not be denied, and however impregnable empires might have appeared at their height… they were as susceptible to the forces of entropy as any other compound or organism.

But questions remain. Has the insistence of entropic forces also played out over the course of our evolutionary history? Does observing how this works show which strategies and decisions do well, and which fail? And how does the endless tension that exists between the zero sum approach of so many things and the non-zero strategy of others become resolved?

Is it possible to see whether some approaches do better than others? And therefore how this has played out throughout the history of the world?

If so, what does this mean for our human cultural evolution?

'I am He, before whom the world trembles, king of kings, and lord of
all I cast my eye on. And everything before my arm is... trouble!'

CHAPTER THIRTEEN

SO, WHAT STRATEGIES SEEMED TO WIN IN THE SWEEP OF THE HUMAN STORY - AND WHY? AND HOW DID THE MANY ATTEMPTS TO RESOLVE THE HOSTILITIES INHERENT IN SOCIAL SYMBIOSES DRIVE OUR PROGRESS? WERE WE EVER ABLE TO SAY WHETHER THINGS WERE WORKING OR FAILING. . . OR EVEN IF THEY WERE 'GOOD' OR 'BAD'?

The anthropologist, Joseph Tainter, saw the success, and inevitable failure, of empires in quasi-thermodynamic terms and he argued in *The Collapse of Complex Societies* that energy usage is central to any understanding of their life cycles. What this meant, he said, was that per capita energy availability could actually drop if a population increased (along with its need for governance) because an empire's agricultural output might be outpaced at the same time. Numbers grew - but resources had to be shared out more thinly. This led empires to weaken, and as they did so, another would take over its energy potential and then merge it into an even bigger superstate.

Jared Diamond was similarly analytical when he argued in *Collapse: How Societies Choose to Fail or Survive*, that the major causes for empires falling apart could be grouped under various headings. Other anthropologists have argued that these might be clustered under three broad threats.

First, there were bound to be environmental problems that could affect an empire's resources. Disasters could lead to hunger, even starvation.

Secondly, they could be affected by either the collapse or hostility of their neighbours, particularly if they were trading partners.

And, thirdly, a society could subside because of its inability to respond to internal problems.

Ha. Haven't we seen these before? Aren't they exactly the factors that decide on the success or failure of species in Nature?

Along with Joseph Tainter and other commentators, Dr Diamond believes that the root causes of all these issues occur when the energy needs of an empire's population exceeds the carrying capacity of its natural resources, particularly its agricultural produce. It all sounds scientific, but it's really what the Reverend Malthus said writ large: that if there are too many people, there comes a point where they can't grow enough grub to go round. When that happens, then death and destruction can set in.

The Romans were a case in point. Professor Tainter claims that their strategy had always been to solve their problems through conquest, because by doing this they'd take over their neighbour's resources in the form of grain, slaves and other surpluses. In time, however, the energy cost of such things as extensive governance, communication networks, a standing army, the many garrisons they needed and so on, all became so enlarged that when mismanagement, or the failure of harvests came along, the problems couldn't be dealt with by just snatching yet more of someone else's territory.

But top-down rulers really only understood the grabbing model. The idea of reinvesting profits into increasing production, or even planning for bad times, was usually alien to them. The constant pressure of satisfying the layers of politicians and nobles beneath them, together with the large numbers of family members and hangers-on, could usually only be met by buying them off - and that soaked up precious resources.

The notion of involving one's populace in a vision of a better and more prosperous future by encouraging non-zero cooperation among them - or even sharing things out a little more fairly - well, that was for the birds.

> **'The values to which people cling most stubbornly under inappropriate conditions are those values that were previously the source of their greatest triumphs.'**
> **Jared Diamond, *Collapse: How Societies Choose to Fail or Succeed***

Historians tend to think of the final demise of the Roman Empire as the watershed that marks the passage from the strategy of forcibly acquiring energy through aggressive warfare, to the new governance models that start to come through with the onset of the Middle Ages. The catalyst for this is generally reckoned to be the development of large, ocean-going ships.

Cultural breakthroughs tended to follow this, because with maritime power came the realisation that territorial expansion didn't just come from marching one's army into a neighbour's land. Now you could incentivise your gangsters to sail overseas, and this could extend a ruler's landholdings by having colonies on the other side of the world as well.

With this new string to their bows, some empires began to identify themselves more as transnational kingdoms - places that tended to be ruled over by high-profile, hands-on monarchs who were avoiding the risks and crippling costs of fighting across land borders. Alongside this, the attractions of naval conquest were also arriving at the same time that the absolutist approach of zero sum rulers was arm wrestling with the increasing importance of merchant-led, bottom-up trading.

The dynamics of these two forces had shifted around for some time as each side attempted to improve its position in their symbiotic relationship, without actually cutting the other off. Now the ancient tussle was being thrown into sharper focus, because the rise in global trading was giving the merchant class the economic clout that rulers couldn't ignore, or simply tax into submission.

Monarchs were generally living beyond their means - and it hurt. The pressure never relented to pay for their vast, fractal-like retinues, the regional nobles, the religious orders and the numerous standing armies. No wonder they were as keen as ever on generating income.

Yet few of them had ever really had to think about where the money came from. Every now and then they'd no doubt have wondered if there was a price to be paid if they overexploited a resentful population, but this was probably rare. It's unlikely they ever imagined the golden goose could actually be killed.

Even if they were giving too little, and taking too much - particularly if it was brutally done - the dark thought that society's underclass might rise up against them would have intruded only during an extremely bad night's sleep. Fear was the instrument that kept the plebs in line, and the volume could always be turned up if needs be. A few of the more enlightened leaders might have tempered this with a common vision of shared greatness, but even they found it had to go hand-in-hand with rather more popular tactics such as 'bread and circuses'.

What do we make of all this from the historical perspective we have now? Don't the ruling class seem weirdly short-sighted to us in their disdain for the very people who were generating the wealth they depended on?

Yet while it's seductive to conclude that they'd all have been zero summers - bad guys made up solely of uncaring, greedy snatchers - it doesn't necessarily follow that the rest of humanity consisted of honest, yeoman stock, sharing what little they had in a culture of non-zero collaboration. That kind of oversimplification is inevitably wide of the mark.

Instead, there would probably have been just as much of a mix between competition and cooperation within the ranks of the top-downers as there was with the bottom-uppers… because human relationships rely on exactly the same kinds of mechanisms that are behind every other symbiosis in the natural world. Genetic evolution may have led to some very remarkable solutions, but the process depends on colossal periods of time, sometimes even millions of years. However, we humans were changing so much around now that our societies were displaying similarly astonishing evolutionary leaps - but in decades, sometimes even in single years.

By the second millennium AD, for example, the tensions inherent in our social relationships were being thrown into ever-sharper focus. The American humourist, PJ O'Rourke, highlights their emergence in his book on Adam Smith, *On The Wealth of Nations*, in which he explains how the old ways of seizing power were coming to an end.

The trouble, as O'Rourke summarises it, was that the nobility's business model had simply become too expensive: 'Power… meant feeding thugs. The more thugs a chieftain could feed, the more powerful he was.' But any power these people had was due to making other people poor, because the amount of land available to be taken by force was finite. And the nobles' land management was dreadful because they despised the process of agriculture, and never thought of incentivising the workers.

With so many mouths to feed, the top dogs were always broke. So they had to fight for more land, and this meant more thugs. An illustration of this, as O'Rourke says, was that: 'Westminster Hall', after the invasion of William the Conqueror, 'wasn't so much a parliament as a dining room.'

Every now and then, though, the underclass would use setbacks to the Big Man's expensive lifestyle to negotiate a better deal for themselves. The loss of lives in the armed conflicts of power struggles, for example, or ghastly pandemics like the Black Death, could lead to real shortages of manpower. And when these happened the price of a day's labour could improve - at least for a bit.

By the time of the Middle Ages, the non-zero trading world was also evolving. The professions were fast becoming more organised: training and qualifications were introduced, and tradespeople and niche artisans were forming themselves into organisations like guilds and livery companies. These set internal examinations to raise standards, even though ostensible improvements like these had paradoxical outcomes.

This was because, on the one hand, they could increase skill levels to the point where members could collectively boost their bargaining power. But on the other the organisations were arguably zero sum in that they limited the number of skilled craftsmen that could be available.

Within the increasingly efficient world that craft specialisms and exchanges were producing, however, the merchant class was in a period of accelerated evolution. They were becoming ever more prosperous and powerful, and in turn the nobility cast increasingly envious glances at their wealth.

PJ O'Rourke's fabulous turn of phrase in *On The Wealth of Nations* continues as he sums up how the presumption of the elite classes was gradually being eroded by their constant need for money. With the squeeze on incomes, he says, their selfish instincts now became so strong that they even began to override any long-term view of their self-preservation.

The merchants saw them coming, of course: 'Critics of free markets assume that there is a fraudulent aspect of capitalism. They're right. We tricked the feudal powers into setting us free and we remained free by continuing to bamboozle them. We used chicanery and sharp dealing to found our cities, we became rich bourgeoisie, and supplied ourselves with creature comforts. We left the aristocracy and their draughty castles throwing chicken bones on the floor. And we were by no means finished with cheating the nobility. We did the worst that can be done to fools: we gave them what they wanted. The towns imported luxury goods and developed arts and crafts. Among these products the nobles discovered things that they'd rather spend their money on than feeding thugs. Feast budgets were trimmed.'

Naturally, the effect of this fundamental shift led the symbiosis between them to become more nuanced.

Now under the growing influence of the merchant class, some European empires like the Venetians and the Genoese were being founded on trade rather than military prowess. The wealth and magnificence of these became legendary, but their city leaders were careful not to pick fights, and avoided threatening the monarchies that surrounded them. Instead, their power came from commerce, and they usually managed to pacify their neighbours by ensuring the safe passage of their goods, rather than by using armed warfare.

Unlike the stratified societies of the top-down model, these city-states had intricate internal structures that set out to limit individual power. This enlightened kind of proto-democracy also led them ensuring their tax and regulatory approach encouraged the growth of trade. Big Men everywhere watched what was going on, jealous of their success, yet slow to copy it. Many were probably too narcissistic to understand how such non-zero collaboration could operate.

Again, it may seem strange to our modern minds, but governing elites have only recently come to terms with the concept of what we now call 'human capital'. It never seemed to have occurred to rulers in those days that there was a difference between productive activities that could generate growth from collaborative trading, and the mass of unproductive soldiers they had standing idle. Or the presumptuous aristocrats and profusion of servants they had hanging onto their coat tails.

In fact, the opposite was more often the case; and the governing class frequently painted themselves into a corner in the way they lived. Instead of encouraging innovation or ingenuity from their people, they went the other way and maintained as wide a gap as possible between the rulers and the actual wealth creators. In their backward-looking minds, this separation continued to bolster their superiority. It generally had the reverse effect, of course, and led to resentment as absurd points of difference between them and the great majority of their people meant that they became ever more distant and aloof.

The sorts of things the Big Men were insisting on included colours that could only be worn by the ruling class, religious rites that only they could understand, languages that only they could speak, castles that only they could own, vast landholdings they wouldn't share with anyone else, and any number of other outward signs they'd dream up to separate themselves from the plebs. All these and many similar nonsenses were designed to ram home the meme that the privileged classes were *credible*.

As examples of this, the powerful elite in England spoke only French for two hundred years after the Norman invasion, something that only a chosen few would have understood. Yellow clothes were outlawed in China, except for the highest strata of the Emperor's court. Latin was the universal European language of religion, medicine and the law, but by prohibiting ordinary people from learning it, governments would limit those who could rise in society.

But why didn't the exploited masses just get up and leave? Why didn't they reject this kind of abuse? Of course, we'd walk now if we were being treated so badly - vote with our feet. But here was the key difference… people in those days simply couldn't. Everyone was a link in society's chain, and bound to each other by family or social dependence. Decisions involved one's betters, hierarchies locked people into 'knowing their place', and wars were fought between groups who were in servitude to their masters. There was never an escape.

Within this framework, monarchs saw no point in educating the masses. Why should they when the people they regarded as unwashed would only have caused trouble if they knew about showers and soap? The last thing the bosses would have wanted was allowing outsiders to start pulling at the levers of power. The zero sum outlook of governing elites ran so deep in them that they were quite incapable of entertaining the idea of $1+1=3$. So why should the common people ever get to own stuff, or to know too much?

Instead of imagining that their peoples' talents and ambitions could ever be a route to increasing income, the ruling class were never able to see merit in anything other than the visible evidence of goodies like gold and silver. Things like this were valuable and easily portable, and it was from these that they thought their prosperity arose. Set against this, slaves, serfs, labourers and so on didn't have to be valued, let alone respected, because they were simply a way of working the land, and growing the country's energy needs.

By the Middle Ages the Big Man's focus had inevitably moved to getting more of the sort of riches he could understand. Large, well-built ships were now sailing ever longer distances, and navigators were bringing back stories of exotic lands far across the oceans. Rumours would have abounded that there were easy pickings to be had from invading and colonising the feeble people that lived in these strange places… and simply taking their limitless treasure.

Bingo, said the top-downers, here's some money for ships… go off and get me shiny stuff that I can run my fingers through while I laugh in triumph. The logic of the market never seemed to trouble them. Kwarsi Kwarteng describes what came next in his book, *War and Gold. A 500 Year History of Empires*. He relates how the Conquistadors, for example, became so greedy for the precious metals of the New World that they flooded the market, using their treasures to hire soldiers and build more ships so that they could grab yet more plunder.

Yet they never invested in productive enterprises and, instead, the squandering of riches by the colonial powers rebounded, and plunged them into debt. In some countries the lessons remain unlearnt, even today. Many continue to destroy their economies by exploiting both their people and their easily obtained assets like oil and timber. Only the more enlightened think of reinvesting this income to secure their futures.

Hold on, though... why were far-flung places like Mexico and Peru such sitting ducks when the Europeans first turned up? Why didn't the home side win? In his books, *The Third Chimpanzee* and, more particularly, *Guns Germs and Steel*, the geographer and historian Jared Diamond poses these very questions when he asks why Eurasians dominated and displaced native Americans, Australians and Africans.

Why wasn't it the other way round?

The memes that so many people of my generation were fed was that the culture and education of Europeans made us in some way better equipped to succeed, perhaps even because of our genetic make-up. That's why we were higher beings. And, no doubt, the endlessly repeated 'survival of the fittest' line would have been trotted out whenever the conversation turned in this direction.

But Professor Diamond argues that the Eurasian advantages weren't in any way functions of biological, intellectual or moral superiority. They were, instead, due to random accidents of nature. Principal among them, he argues, was that the East-West axis of the Continental landmass favoured the expansion of the tribes and peoples who lived there, because the geographic layout implied that more species of plants and animals could be domesticated. This meant that even though agriculture had sprung up at roughly the same time across the globe, the geographical advantages of the Eurasian races were always going to give them a head start.

Perhaps the most important of these advantages stemmed from the available grains and pulses which gave the early people a high carbohydrate and protein rich vegetation. These led them to be better fed and healthier, with larger settlements and more organised structures when the global race was on to become top dog.

Why did it matter so much? It was because, in spite of its great size, the East-West landmass had similar latitudes and growing conditions, and this meant everywhere shared roughly similar climates and seasons. Human migration was easier, people exchanged plants and animals as they did so, and they also brought with them the ideas that were so necessary for profitable interactions and trading. And as these settlers exchanged things and built their larger communities, they increasingly stimulated innovation.

> 'The history of civilisation is the history of the expansion of particularly
> attractive cultural and social patterns through the conversion of barbarians
> to modes of life they found superior to their own.'
> William McNeil, *The Rise of the West*

On the other hand, Africa and the Americas were held back because they shared the same problems of extreme climate variation along their long North-South axes. Critically, this meant there were always challenges their migrating people would have to overcome when they tried to introduce their crops.

Not only did the native species prove harder to sow, but the settlers would also have had to contend with the absence of working beasts, something that ensured humans couldn't escape the hard labour of agriculture. This, and the problems of transporting people and goods over long distances, were always going to limit the

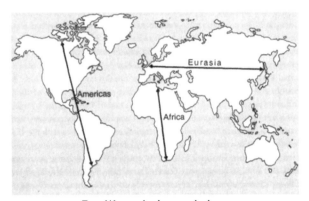

East-West... that's got to be best.

pioneers' capacity for working the land.

But these factors weren't the only ones that put the early inhabitants at such a disadvantage to the colonists.

First, Dr Diamond says, the invading forces had guns that brought them military superiority and conquest.

Secondly, they imported Eurasian germs that the indigenous people had never encountered: deadly diseases that generally arose as viruses that could pass from animals to humans. Smallpox, measles and even influenza originated from livestock, and while the occupying soldiers would have developed a herd immunity to them over the centuries, the local communities had none. As a consequence, it's thought that as much as 95% of the New World's populations died as a result of European diseases. A combination of these two factors meant that any contact almost always ended in genocide.

Then, last, the later invention of steel transport and its applications in things like ships and trains brought about the final stages of colonial domination.

Set against this, Europe was particularly fortunate in the way it was geographically spread. Jared Diamond's theories suggest that because the continent had so many natural boundaries from its rivers, coastlines and mountain ranges, European nations were comparatively small and often close to each other. This proximity led them to compete very quickly, and helpful innovations and inventions would then have been quickly spread.

> '**The disagreements that continue today to frustrate even modest attempts at European unification… are symptomatic of Europe's ingrained commitment to disunity.**'
> **Jared Diamond, *Guns, Germs and Steel***

Every point that Professor Diamond so brilliantly exposes in his books always seems to lead back to descriptions of how it's the expansion of non-zero relationships that's been so central to our success. When people get together they talk, they exchange things, they share problems and they come up with solutions.

This is a process that leads to what Matt Ridley would so colourfully describe as 'ideas having sex'. By this he means that when humans are trading, there's always the incentive for someone to think of a better way of doing things. One only has to look around to see the proof of this. And any glance at our history shows that there's nothing our big brains and natural ingenuity equip us for more than finding smarter solutions.

How does this come about? Well, it largely depends on people communicating, and therefore becoming motivated to find ways around roadblocks. Helpful conditions shot forward when larger societies emerged because people were increasingly part of extensive specialisation and exchange networks. Problem-solvers were more able to discuss things that needed fixing, and this would inevitably have led people to improve on the old methods.

By the time of the Middle Ages, for example, even though the great majority of people wouldn't have been able to read, it still didn't stop them from developing astonishing advances in communication. Quite literally, they were putting their heads together.

It's hardly surprising, therefore, that when historians point to the improvements in food supply that were arising at around this time, the major reasons were breakthroughs such as the invention of the wheelbarrow, the heavy plough, tidal mills, the concept of three field crop rotation and the introduction of stern-mounted rudders that allowed larger ships to open up international trade.

As for muscle power, possibly the major breakthrough came when some unknown genius invented a harness that didn't throttle the horse. Now this more biddable beast could replace the lumbering ox as a draught animal, agricultural productivity accelerated.

> 'The question of what individual nations can do on their own
> is more or less pointless - the key is the universal brain, as it is
> now, or the regional collective brain as it was then.'
> **Robert Wright,** *Nonzero*

The consequences of these kinds of trading forces were all leading to ever greater interaction and sophisticated exchanges. From these came their inevitable offspring: greater prosperity, increased levels of trust, and as night follows day, far more recognisable moral codes.

But while this changing social landscape might look like a uniformly positive trend, problems were always going to arise when it happened, because the more that people interacted in trustworthy communities, the more that the bad guys would try to take advantage of the reduced levels of suspicion and punishment.

How did societies usually respond to these threats? They did it by introducing laws that attempted to prevent the takers from working against the common good. The underlying way of doing this has always been to make it difficult for transgressors by *identifying* them, and then pushing them to the margins of society. But how were they being exposed? Mainly through the expansion of reliable shared information that allowed people to tell each other who the exploiters were. This meant cooperative people could *avoid* them. And, as non-zero cooperation was now expanding in societies with the growth of trade, so people were becoming increasingly able to make better choices about who they dealt with.

So what were the big lessons to emerge from these great directional forces? Were there parallels with the patterns of behaviour that genetic evolution had produced in the natural world?

While it's probably a mistake to claim too slavish a similarity, among the most fascinating of insights is the degree to which apparently damaging changes to society can later turn out to be of benefit, in just the same way that deleterious mutations can alter an organism for the better. And, conversely, the opposite can also be true.

The effects of this happening are plain if one looks back at how events have unfolded throughout our human journey. The Big Man's greed and his lust for power, for example, may have led to ghastly conflicts, but they were also directly responsible for cultural unification and the expansion of non-zero opportunities. That has to be good, one might think.

But this growth, in turn, encouraged devious types to break peoples' trust in larger societies. That must be bad.

However, because these actions lead to reputational damage for defectors and cheats, the resulting exposure is bound to diminish their mate-signally attractions. Good, because then their anti-social impulses will reduce the influence they have in society - and in the gene pool - and the proportion of cooperative genes will increase.

And round and round the cycle might go, yet the overall direction of travel will always be *upwards*: to further complexity, to improved security for the gene, and to ever greater non-zero cooperation within the biosphere.

The end result of this logic is that even when human history shows our decision-making leading to incontrovertibly bad choices and collapses, we can still profit from the outcomes. Cultural evolution can be just as effective in throwing up 'productive mistakes' as errors in DNA replication can stimulate genetic benefits. Just as these mutations can later be seen to have worked for an organism's ultimate benefit, so too can setbacks to human progress open up new opportunities.

This is what our long story has shown time and again.

Sometimes the errors we make can even result in what social commentators call 'creative destruction', when wholly new ideas take root in the same way that novelty can bloom after an extinction event. The worst calamities can even propel a society forward, because they can produce changes that no carefully prepared strategy could ever have achieved.

And so, as one looks at the underlying currents of our human development, although we share with other life forms our ability to range in our behaviour from uncaring parasitism to altruism, contradictions nonetheless abound. The end result? Surely one's left simply reflecting on the core truth that competition and cooperation may be in constant conflict, yet they are also in symbiotic union as the two forces respond to the demands of the 1st and 2nd Laws of Thermodynamics. This is as evident in the most sophisticated rationales of human decision-making as it is in the life choices of basic organisms.

Where one can point with the greatest certainty to the parallel paths of evolution, however, is the way that our lives are all affected by external factors. Societies may develop in rational ways, but they can be just as quickly knocked off course as the security of a species can be imperiled if it's faced with environmental change or competitive pressure. Just as with them, so our cultural progression shows that it isn't the challenges that matter, but how our societies respond to them.

Perhaps the most interesting inference is to see how hugely detrimental it is to deflect external problems by ducking them. Isolation is always more damaging than adaptation, and avoiding pressures can be a fatal choice. This is the lesson that provides the explanation for some of the oddest mysteries of our human story.

Foremost among them, anthropologists and historians have long discussed the questions over why China fell apart when it seemed to have the world at its feet? Or why the aboriginal people of Tasmania should have disappeared so soon after the first European settlers arrived? Both of these examples illustrate how vital it is in life not to cut oneself off from outside influences - but why?

China could be said to represent one pole on the scale of case histories. But why did it come apart so *quickly*? After all, at roughly the time that the Middle Ages were taking place in Europe, the hard working and entrepreneurial Chinese had taken their vast territory to global dominance.

Among other assets there, the country had the greatest fleet the world had ever seen and this, together with a number of extraordinary inventions like porcelain, high explosives, the magnetic compass and the mass production of silk, were just a few of the things that had taken the nation decades ahead of its nearest competitors.

As ever, though, the Big Man's constant need for income would cock things up. Arguably unaware of how advanced they were, the Ming rulers came up with a strategy in the 15th century that was straight out of the Mafia's playbook: find a few feeble patsies and then demand protection money from them. What a good idea this seemed to the Emperor - and terrifying war junks were sent out on shock and awe missions to threaten the country's less powerful neighbours.

But the Chinese super fleet made the mistake of not only scaring foreigners with their technological advances, but of also allowing outsiders to see things they had on board like their beautiful textiles and gorgeous porcelain bowls. Far from rooting the foreign devils to the spot in fear, the ships had the unexpected effect of acting as floating trade exhibitions for the country's wares.

This had the unintended consequence of opening up huge interest in its goods, and before long, instead of shelling out protection money, merchants were opening up trade routes, foreign harbours and enthusiastic customers.

What was the problem, though? Surely this would have set the Chinese on the path to global economic supremacy? If the country had both military might and any number of products to trade, why didn't it supplant their weak regional competitors?

The problem was that none of these glaring advantages was ever enough to stop the paranoid instincts of a plainly rattled leadership. Their heads were always uneasy at night because they'd hung on too long to their top-down, overly stratified power structures, and had instead allowed space to develop for the growing forces of non-zero cooperation.

With their usual attention to detail, the Chinese governance model might have been a highly effective centralised system, yet its inflexible, zero sum approach had had the effect of strangling internal communication, and along with this - innovation.

The suffocating bureaucracy that ran the country had simply gone too far. It was micromanaging every detail of the country's affairs and the resulting control-freakery had become so deeply rooted that it took the oxygen out of ordinary people's lives.

The country even had, for instance, a formalised, talent spotting operation that toured the country looking for children of outstanding intelligence that could be groomed as trainee mandarins, and educated in the arts of government. For many years this system added layer upon layer of unbending bureaucrats to the same two-word instruction on how best to serve the imperial model: *no change.*

This is exactly the sort of stultification that'll kill an economy - and it did. Stagnation is death: if you're not going forward, you're going backwards. Without the challenges that lead to the exchange of ideas that allow societies to change and evolve, then initiative and innovation will decline.

But what had made China's rulers so blinded by fear? As elsewhere, it had been the pressure coming down on them from the men-on-the-make: the non-zero middle men merchants. In the Confucian world order, merchants were viewed as parasites, even lower forms of life than the way that European rulers viewed them. The success of the Imperial Fleet may have opened the way to feed gorgeous products into the Silk Road… but the administrative class now realised that foreign traders were responding by selling so many things back to them that they were undermining the empire's balance of payments.

Arguably even more damaging than this, these same foreigners were bringing with them dangerous stories about how much more equitable the social contract was in other countries.

In short, not only was China overtrading, but seditious ideas were being planted in its subjects' heads. The debt burden was also getting out of control. Money might be coming in from taxes, but high levels of corruption were hollowing out the hierarchical system, something that was being made worse by the gigantic and non-productive cost of building the Great Wall. Constructing this had been a panicky decision aimed at keeping the Mongol hordes out, but the cost overruns were becoming so utterly ruinous that no amount of increased trading could ever balance the books.

In 1433 the Hongxi emperor took decisive action. At precisely the time that Europe's vision was turning outwards, with ships being commissioned to explore overseas opportunities, the Chinese court turned inwards.

Whatever the cost, it was decided that foreign influence and goods had to be kept out. A decree was issued and the glorious fleet - 250 of the world's largest ships - was never to sail again. Each of them had been larger than Vasco da Gama's flagship, yet those that weren't burnt were now left at their anchors to rot.

Foreign ships were also banned from entering Chinese harbours, and trade and outside contact dried up. But closing the counting was a disastrous move for China and as the world changed around them, it now embarked on a long economic decline that would eventually lead to starvation, revolution and six hundred years of humiliation.

'Within a few generations, the Chinese allowed their naval and merchant fleets to wither; in 1500 an imperial edict made the construction of vessels with more than two masts a capital offense. In 1525, another decree forbade

the building of any oceangoing vessel. Where navies are absent, pirates pillage.'

Yuval Noah Harari, *Homo Deus*

Although China had seemingly made the wrong choices, it's possible that we're now seeing it return to pick up the threads of its destiny. As Peter Frankopan says in his world history, *The Silk Road*, we could well be witnessing: '...the birthing pains of a region that once dominated the intellectual, cultural and economic landscape and which is now re-emerging. We are seeing the signs of the world's centre of gravity shifting - back to where it lay for millennia.'

China's near neighbour, Japan, would make the exact same mistakes nearly four hundred later - and experience precisely the same outcomes. Whenever the country's islands opened their ports, their culture and economy grew. Whenever they closed, they stagnated.

Similar outcomes were to be seen throughout the world wherever restrictive policies were imposed. In case after case, when countries shut out information flows and efficient transport systems, they then threw away their chances of creating non-zero opportunities and market expansion.

Anthropologists point to one of the starkest examples of this in the history of the Australian island of Tasmania. The process of stultification in this case, however, was the result of environmental change rather than top-down strategic orders. But the result was the same. As Jared Diamond was to describe it: 'Tasmanian history is a study of human isolation unprecedented except in science fiction - namely, complete isolation from other humans for 10,000 years.'

Why had it come about? The problem arose because the Bass Straits separating the island from mainland Australia had widened over the millennia, and the aboriginal population there had become cut off from outside contact. The consequence of the lack of stimulation meant its inhabitants never made the jump from hunter-gathering to the larger populations that emerged with agriculture.

Total numbers on the island therefore probably never rose higher than a few thousand, and without the genetic vigour and challenges that come with human progress, the tribes of Tasmania were to become a sad example of how the deprivation of external stimuli will put a species into terminal decline.

By the time the Dutch navigator Abel Tasman arrived in 1642, the population had been reduced to a pitiful condition. Not only had they never developed the simplest trapping or fishing equipment, but they'd also lost the skills of their ancestors. The colonists found they had no idea, for instance, of how to make fish hooks or spears, boomerangs or even cold weather clothes. Nor, amazingly, could they understand the concepts of specialist labour or barter.

Over on the other side of the world, however, a similarly obscure group of people had managed to achieve the opposite outcome. These were the inhabitants of the archipelago of Tierra del Fuego, who'd been cut off from the coast of South America in the same way as Tasmania, and yet its people had managed to stay in contact with their mainland relations.

By doing this, their levels of innovation and hunting technologies had evolved in roughly parallel ways. Charles Darwin studied them during his famous trip in *HMS Beagle*, and found that they used barter to exchange their own surpluses for things they wanted from the outsiders. He was astonished, for instance, to see how highly they regarded the metal nail he offered them.

The clear inference that anthropologists come to when they compare these and other case histories is the one that's seen in so many other spheres of life… that if a species doesn't develop even rudimentary non-zero collaborative exchanges, then it condems itself to irreversible decline.

But if one returns to the wider picture of cultural evolution, how was the gulf between the small proportion that made up the ruling elite, and the great majority of people in the underclass ever going to be narrowed? Outright rebellion, the withdrawal of labour and the pressure of bottom-up cooperation might be the principal mechanisms, but these responses were only rarely used because even the slightest protest invariably provoked savage reprisals.

Any progress that might have led to a fairer division in the human symbiosis was glacial. Trading, the growth of skills, craftsmen and the sheer energy of the lower layers of society simply took too long to be appreciated by entrenched, arrogant leaders who had no incentive to do anything other than keep their people docile and obedient. While the merchant echelon might continue to be viewed as a political menace, they were always a necessary evil because governance systems relied on their tax revenue. By the late Middle Ages, the only reason the non-productive, ruling class networks continued to survive was because of this income.

A comparison with the natural world is, once more, almost exact. The analogy of the benefits - and yet inherent hostilities - seen in human societies was by now acting in the same way as any number of Nature's symbioses. The human species might have also progressed by making 1+1=3… yet by the 17th century, the imbalances in society meant they were operating at more like $1.5 + 0.5 = 3$. And this was bound to eventually lead to trouble.

How was change ever going to come, though, in a world in which all the levers of power depended on knowledge and position? Why on earth would the top dogs ever throw a bone to the lower strata of society - and why would the zero summers ever see things in a non-zero way?

It's difficult to imagine what would break the logjam… yet something was coming down the track that could only have arisen out of human ingenuity and our addiction to novelty. It was exactly the kind of social mutation that makes us so capable of fast change.

It was going to upset everything, throw the hierarchical certainties in the air and unleash civil wars and revolutions that would last for three hundred years. Along the way it would totally reshape our societies.

What was it? Well, in a small city in Germany a young man had a dream…

The early publishers learnt quickly that they could
cheat to make the printed word look like
an expensive scribe's handwriting. Here's a page
from the 1460s that even combines a woodcut
that could be coloured in later to look like an
expensive original.

CHAPTER FOURTEEN

IT WAS TIME FOR THE SEVENTH REVOLUTION - SOMETHING THAT WOULD BLOW THE WORLD APART BY COMPLETELY ALTERING THE BALANCE OF HUMAN SYMBIOSES. IT LOOKED LIKE A MINOR TECHNICAL ADVANCE... BUT IT WAS TO LEAD TO THE KNOWLEDGE REVOLUTION, AND WITH IT A COMPLETE REBALANCING OF HOW SOCIETIES WORKED

Much as his jaw would have jutted and his chinstrap wobbled, even the most ardent of rookie Roman legionaries would probably have offered up a silent prayer or two as he bellowed out his oaths to serve the Empire. Here's hoping, he would understandably have been thinking, that he could somehow see out his twenty-five years of service and be rewarded with that nice little farm they'd promised him for volunteering. But could he also, please, be posted somewhere that wasn't too much of a *nightmare*?

There were quite a few horrible places to choose from. From the burning heat of the southern desert to the knife-like winds of Perthshire, there were rather too many that wouldn't have been much fun. But worse than any of these, it was generally agreed that the hellhole you didn't want to be sent to was the bleak, wooded region in the north-westerly corner of Magna Germania.

The place had become a byword for horror. It was here that early in the first century the Battle of the Teutoburg Forest had been fought.

Germany 1 Italy 0.

A ruthless chieftain called Arminius had swapped sides, and then managed to form an alliance of the warrior tribes that stopped the Roman invasion in its tracks. In a brilliant series of fast striking guerilla movements, he'd used the dense woods and the cover of appalling weather to slaughter around 20,000 of Rome's crack soldiers. Three entire legions of hardened veterans had been annihilated, together with countless camp followers. Not a single person returned home to tell the tale.

The body blow this handed out to the dream of Roman dominance sent such a shock to the Empire's German strategy that it changed its outlook from conquest to containment. Ever since that dreadful defeat, its armies had been on a continuous war footing and a massive base had been constructed at the confluence of the great waterways of the Rhine and the Main. It was from here - *castrum* Mogontiacum - that the army could monitor the river traffic as it passed, as well as using the fortress as a base to ride out from and suppress the threats of the barbarian tribes.

Yet in one of those delicious ironies that litter history, a thousand years after the German hordes would later undermine the Western Empire, Mogontiacum would evolve under the same non-zero sum forces that had been changing societies everywhere. Now the bullying days were over, yet its strategic location had led to it becoming an important trading centre, long since renamed Mainz.

By the middle of the 15th century, a city that had once known only the brutality and inflexibility of military occupation was to become the cultural midwife to a whole new era of art, philosophy, religious thinking, literature, scientific knowledge... and social justice. Unknown to anyone at the time, Mainz was destined to be the springboard for Europe to become the centre of global innovation - and the reason the fulcrum of economic power moved so decisively away from Asia and towards the Western world.

Why, what happened? In a couple of words, *mass printing*. In one fewer... *information*.

Information was the one thing that the Big Men, generals and religious authorities would have dreaded above all else.

Information was what led people to know things; worse, to think about them, to weigh up the evidence, and possibly even to ask what the governing class was doing to earn its corn. Were their rulers right in what they were telling their people to think? Or were the elites the medieval equivalent of the Wizard of Oz, all deep voice and barked orders, yet hiding behind a flimsy wall of myths and terror tactics?

The invention of large-scale printing was the spark that would shine a light on these questions. It would be the first step on the journey to satisfy our unquenchable thirst for knowledge - and to push back against the Big Man's control over our lives. Information? It seems we can't get enough of it now - and once the idea of mass communication had taken root with printing, then the progression to pamphlets, newspapers, books, radio, television, the internet and a hundred and one other ways of sharing our thoughts, were all simply a matter of time and technical progress.

> '**What the world is today, good and bad, it owes to Gutenberg.**
> **Everything can be traced to this source.**'
> **Mark Twain,** *in a letter of 1900*

But back to the early days, and sadly it was yet another case of the poor old Chinese inventing the big stuff - and then failing to take advantage of it. As far back as 220 AD they'd arrived at the idea of making blocks out of wood or porcelain that could then be inked and pressed onto fabric. A few hundred years later, there'd even been attempts by the Koreans and the Southern Chinese to lash together individual symbols into a frame, and use it to print the pages of a book.

The roadblock they'd always come up against, however, was the same one they'd encountered so often with their written language: there were simply too many symbols to make the idea work. They tried any number of ways of solving the problem, even creating a series of ideograms in either wood or porcelain. But the concept of printing on any kind of scale faded, and then joined the pile of inventions that were cast aside and later forgotten when China retreated from the world.

But how had Europeans been communicating? By handwriting - always a colossally laborious exercise and only made possible by having an entire class of expert scribes. These were the specialists who'd take dictation or copy out the ruler's written orders, laws and chronicles. The fastest of them might turn out two short books a year.

Frequently they were members of monastic orders, sometimes women, and they'd take as much as eighteen months to produce a large bible or liturgical missal, awash with its copperplate writing and luxurious illustrations. It was a hugely expensive way of copying the written word, using up massive amounts of manpower and the hides of hundreds of animals to supply the parchment or vellum for just a single volume. The Black Death in the mid 14th century was also a particularly bad blow as it devastated so many of the monasteries.

Even within Europe, however, the idea of printing wasn't entirely new. Wooden blocks had been engraved on for some time, but they'd only been used for such frivolities as playing cards, or for reproducing old master prints.

This all meant that the idea of using books to exchange stories or beliefs on any scale hadn't really progressed since the onset of agriculture had so changed human societies. There were handwritten letters, of course, but these were rarely copied for distribution, and particularly not if they contained subversive thoughts. Even with the rudimentary postal services that existed at the time, the cost and time of producing anything that allowed ideas to be circulated was both slow, and almost invariably local.

Then, sometime around 1450, a young goldsmith in Mainz called Johannes Gutenberg began to resurrect the Chinese technique of arranging different letters in a frame. What intrigued him was the realisation that if he could only crack the various mechanical problems, he could move the *same* bits of type around and put them in different places, depending on what was being printed.

In many ways he was combining old ideas with more recent technologies. Parchment was the principal medium for recording important documents but this was being superseded by new processes that were making paper that was both durable and flexible.

The Renaissance artists of Italy had also recently come up with new chemical formulas for their oil based paints, and before long these breakthroughs had allowed Gutenberg to cook up inks that were viscous enough to stick to metal. As for the press itself, the fruit pulping industry had invented different kinds of screw mechanisms that he could easily adapt to bring down the pressure needed to make imprints.

1450. Gutenberg invents the paper jam.

The Secrets of Life - Book Two

Where Gutenberg's genius changed everything, though, was when he used his metalworking skills to come up with an alloy to make the perfect typeface. His breakthrough was a combination of tin, lead, antimony, copper and bismuth that was strong enough to last repeated impressions and yet still allowed the ink surface to be transferred onto the new kinds of softer and more absorbent papers. Incredibly, the same metal alloy he developed for his original letters was still being used many hundreds of years later.

But there was another factor that would move the centre of global culture decisively towards Europe - and that was the limited number of letters in the standard alphabet. Instead of the thousands of characters that had made the Chinese give the idea up as unworkable, Gutenberg realised that he could stick any combination of characters into his hand mould. The technique became known as 'movable type', and he immediately saw that the idea could be used for a whole range of different results.

Like many a revolutionary inventor before and since, however, it seems he was always pretty flakey when it came to money, and equally quick to fall out with his business partners. Nonetheless there must have been enough cash coming in for him to design a number of different typefaces and, in the early days, he found that printing up poems and song lyrics put his name about and sold best.

By the time he died in 1469, it's thought he had over 250 separate letterboxes in his type case, as well as any number of special characters such as gap blanks, line breakers and punctuation marks. He'd also discovered that types and fonts could give a script meaning.

Poetry and love stories would look romantic in flowery italics, Gothic typefaces were able to make the page look as scholarly as a scribe's handwriting, orders and warnings would shout at people when they were printed in large capital letters, and up-market thinking was best expressed by posh-looking letters. These usually had decorative little lines stuck on the end of letters called serifs. As Marshall McLuhan was later to say in *Understanding Media*: 'The medium is the message' - because how things looked was also part of the story. Mass printing and mass communication, as we know them, were underway.

Of course, it didn't take long before Gutenberg came to the notice of the authorities. Nothing was ever a secret for long in those days. What did they think? They loved it! How could that be, one wonders... surely the ruling class can't have been blind to the kind of damage that mass knowledge could bring to their legends and presumptions?

Well, none of this seems to have occurred to them. Instead, the command and control forces simply imagined they'd found a better alternative to scribal copying. What everyone from Big Men to bishops liked about the new technology was the way it could improve the quality and accuracy of books. Almost overnight, spelling could be standardised, words were made easier to read, errors were reduced (monks were reckoned to make as much as a mistake a page) and the same information could be relied on to fall in the same place. Numbering, contents pages and indices now became common. Best of all, the price of a book plummeted.

By 1455, the Church was commissioning Gutenberg to produce bibles and Catholic prayer books at a fraction of the prices they'd previously had to pay for them. Before he'd come along, these could only be afforded by institutions like universities and monasteries. Now they were coming in at a snip... well, snipish anyway. While a paper version might only be a fifth of the price of a hand-written parchment manuscript, they were still out of the reach of all except the wealthiest churches and noblemen.

The Church could only see things from its own viewpoint. Printing was a boon not a threat. Its leaders convinced themselves that religious instruction would be enhanced by a wider circulation of their regulations and rubrics.

Monarchies were similarly blinkered, seeing printing as greasing the gears of state, and increasing their control over what people were told and believed. Stories about how wonderful they all were could now be more frequently repeated. Surely their grip would tighten, rather than be threatened?

Hmm. How wrong could they be? The genie of mass communication flew out of the bottle and printing presses began to spring up everywhere. Even the largest of the new publishers found they could ramp up production with just a handful of craftsmen. In only the two or three decades up to 1480, printers went from being rare to becoming commonplace. Over a hundred of them were operating in Germany alone by this time, and there are records of others spreading to as many as a dozen other European countries. No doubt there was a Mr Pronta around somewhere.

In as little as fifty years after Gutenberg's first experiments, it's thought there were presses operating throughout the whole of Western Europe. The fires of change, of questioning and liberal opinion were well and truly lit.

But could anyone actually read, you're probably asking? What was the big deal if only the religious leaders and governing class could understand what was being put out?

Curiously, it seems that far more people were literate than one would have thought. It's true that general readership had gone backwards since the days when most Romans not in the labouring classes would have had a fairly reasonable stab at understanding the Empire's written laws and orders. This was a time when the majority of people had some kind of rudimentary skill that let them know what was carved on the various plinths and buildings.

Even so, by about 1500, European countries had percentage literacy rates in the high teens, and although this would have been almost entirely made up of the upper echelons of society, the trickle-down effect was taking root. By around the same time, for example, it's been estimated that something like twenty million printed volumes were in circulation throughout Europe, and the number was going to rise tenfold over the course of the next century.

This uplift in scale had the effect of frequently doubling and even trebling literacy in certain countries, particularly England, as well as making individual authors enormously influential. Clever people such as theologians and philosophers began to circulate their ideas to an audience that was hungry for intellectual stimulation and willing to fork out for it. By the time of his death in 1536, for instance, Erasmus is thought to have sold something like 750,000 copies of his work. Thinking was suddenly big business.

And with thinking came questioning. Hardly surprising one might have concluded, because the social symbioses between the haves and the have-nots had been coming under increasing strain for some time.

The soft underbelly of the 'what are you doing to deserve being so high and mighty' system was undoubtedly religion. And problems were looming. The monasteries and the priest class had by now become exceedingly fat on the proceeds of their vast landholdings, yet their unholy alliance with the ruling class was about to rebound on them.

The unwritten contract the Church had always proposed to the downtrodden was that life might be ghastly, but if you kept your nose clean then there'd be heavenly rewards at the end of it. That was fine... but there seemed to be a different arrangement for the nobs. For this lucky bunch the Catholic hierarchy had cooked up an extremely complex collection of dodges that allowed people to pay up front for a speedy check-out when they were in Purgatory. Having enough cash meant you did less time.

The racket was called simony and it was widespread throughout most of Western Europe. What was becoming increasingly clear, however, was that the Church had overreached itself in selling these 'indulgences' - because they were only going to the people who could afford them. At the other end of the social spectrum, the poor unwashed had been growling for some time at just how unfair this all was. Not only did they have a lousy time of it when they were alive, but they couldn't escape from further horrors when they died. Why wasn't this the same for everyone?

Now the dissidents within the clergy joined the fight against this nonsense - as well as the mass of other corrupt and un-Christian practices that were being used to provide the vast incomes enjoyed by the Vatican and the monasteries. One man, above all, was campaigning to bring it all to an end.

Now the penny dropped, and he saw he could use the opportunities that printing made possible to circulate his ideas. He drew up his objections - and nailed them to a church door in the Saxon town of Wittenberg.

His name was Martin Luther and it only took four months for his '95 theses' to be translated into his native German, and for printed copies to be spreading throughout the entire country. Within a few more weeks they'd reached the rest of Europe - and the Reformation was underway.

What made Luther so unstoppable was that he followed up the publication of his theses by translating the Bible and other religious texts into German. This was a completely revolutionary idea because he was now using a language that the common man could understand. Prior to this the vast majority of the population, if they'd wanted to know something, would have had to ask a priest. He was often the only person they knew that was educated enough to read Latin. Now they could read these things for themselves or, at least, find a literate lay-person who could read them out aloud.

Luther created a speed of opposition to the Church that its leaders could have never imagined. Within his lifetime, the publications he produced are reckoned to have had a total print run of something like 300,000. Goodness knows how many people these copies would then have been passed around to.

The protest movement expanded. People even began calling themselves Protestants, and Germans were now thinking that God had given them the printing press so that their religious objections could be made.

> 'The three great elements of modern civilisation:
> gunpowder, printing and the Protestant religion.'
> Thomas Carlyle, *Critical and Miscellaneous Essays.*

Versions of the Bible in vernacular languages were by now springing up everywhere. In 1526 William Tyndale published his translation from the original Greek into English so that: '… ere many years, I will cause a boy who drives a plough to know more of the scriptures than you do'. Ten years later he was martyred. His last words were nothing if not a prophetic warning to the ruling class: 'Lord!' he cried out. 'Open the King of England's eyes!'

But if some of Europe's monarchs had their eyes closed then there were others who were seeing only too clearly what was going on - and didn't like it at all. Instead of recognising that democratising knowledge was the way to unlock their people's collective genius, they could only see social problems being unleashed. Yet if they'd only understood the long-term damage they were inflicting on themselves by standing in its way, they might have thought twice about ever limiting free speech.

The Turkish Sultan did not - and in 1515 he made using a printing press an offence punishable by death. The entire Muslim world soon followed.

Why were they so quick to do that? It was because the religion's approach to its followers was instinctively controlling, and its clerisy would therefore have been against the dissemination of any form of message other than its own. It's hardly surprising where this led. When historians discuss the departure of Islam from much of Western culture, they'll frequently suggest that the prohibition of the press was the point at which the rich poetry and scientific scholarship of the past gave way to the inward-directed authoritarianism that continues to the present day.

> 'Two huge cultural developments hampered the growth and acceptance
> of Islam - and to some extent continue to do so. The first was that they banned
> the printing press so they could control outside influences. And, secondly,
> their justice system became warped by bribery.
> Robert Wright, *Nonzero*

As the threat that mass information posed became clearer, the authorities descended on their favourite whipping boys, the Jews. Now anyone with Jewish heritage was being attacked and banned from joining the new guilds. Many were accused of being behind the new technology, to line their pockets as they undermined Christianity. By the late 16th century the Germans had become so rattled by it all that they were closing the stable door as the horse was just a dim spot on the horizon.

At this point the authorities began to stamp down on the print shops, but the industry simply upped sticks and moved to Venice.

Now in the hands of Europe's most astute traders, the second stage of the print revolution took off. Being the smartest people on the planet, the Venetians quickly realised that the market wasn't going to be for tiny numbers of massive bibles, but for small and cheap books that could fit into a man's pocket.

It was this insight that saw the general public's appetite for the Greek classics boom. The Venetians were right, the market grew fast and the Renaissance mushroomed alongside it. Printing presses spread throughout Italy - and as the country's entrepreneurs had already pioneered the papermaking industry, they now set about putting the two together and becoming the European leaders in publishing. The Church's grip weakened further under the sheer volume of the output that followed. More and more secular books flooded out and, with them, Italy's economy took off.

Did one lead to the other? Did printing catalyse trade?

Yes, without question, has to be the simple conclusion. Merchants were now working off better information, they could publicise their products to wider markets, and they could operate internationally as the printing houses also offered translation services. Taken together, the knowledge-based economies were up and running, and European markets began to break away from the sludgy, top-down strictures that had so often limited the Asian suppliers.

Print led to information, information to trade, trade to non-zero activities, non-zero to larger markets, larger markets to ever more investment in innovation, innovations to growth, and growth to economic leadership.

Printing lay at the heart of this. The new guilds and craft unions were increasingly improving standards and, as trade grew, so non-zero activities evolved towards ever higher levels of social cooperation. The cat of information was out of the bag of deference - and with it the pressure on monarchies grew.

How did they respond? In the daftest way possible. Instead of entering into revenue sharing arrangements with the merchant class, taking a slice of what passed through them in return for specific rights and laws, they snatched instead at one-off payments for issuing licences. The merchants, as usual, saw them coming and agreed.

Of course, the up-front income this generated was handy for the ruling elite as it kept their flashy show on the road. But, yet again, they'd failed to spot that trade, information and knowledge would all ultimately undermine their authority and control. And, indeed, it didn't take long for people to be questioning how and why they were being so suffocatingly micromanaged.

So, what happened next?

Well pretty much what would happen if you asked any of the parties in a symbiosis if they'd like to change the arrangement. Would they wish to renegotiate how they split their benefits? Ha, what would the mitochondria in cells have to say to the nuclei if there was an opportunity for change? Maynard Smith said that the relationship was subject to ruthless 'metabolic exploitation' - so wouldn't a bit of a rebalance be welcomed if it were possible?

Or what about the cyanobacteria in plants: 'Hey, you wouldn't even be here without me!' Or the countless subjects of parasitic attacks? Would they agree that they were being treated fairly?

My guess is the result would be the same as what now broke out in human societies.

Trouble.

'And is your father a richer hee or a poorer hee?'

CHAPTER FIFTEEN

IF MASS PRINTING WAS INDEED TO BE SUCH AN AGENT OF CHANGE, THEN WHAT WAS THE CHANGE - AND WHERE WOULD IT LEAD?

In their great book, *A Social History of the Media: from Gutenburg to The Internet*, Asa Briggs and Peter Burke list out the five different ways people began to read once books became widely available. All of them were going to have a deep and lasting effect on our cultural evolution, on how we viewed ourselves, on how we chose to behave with each other, and perhaps most importantly of all, on how the relationship between the boss class and those at the bottom would evolve after so many centuries of being unquestioned.

With the flood of new books that emerged with the spread of the printing press, Briggs and Burke say that reading became a *private* occupation, and that silent study would now encourage humans to think. Before this there'd only really been oral communication, unless someone like a cleric happened to be authorised to read the Bible to himself. If a person said something really important, then it was only recorded if the community could afford a scribe. Now the new kind of silent reading allowed people to be solitary as they absorbed a written message, and this led to people coming to their own conclusions, rather than being swept along in the groupthink that inevitably came with things being pronounced.

Secondly, reading began to take general knowledge to far higher levels. Not only were there many more books available, but instead of reading things from start to finish, people now began to consume selected bits of longer works. By doing this they greatly extended what they knew.

Thirdly, the reading public began to interpret things more creatively, frequently in ways that the author might not have wanted them to. Next, it led to people being more critical in their opinions. And, last, it encouraged them to think 'dangerously', examining more deeply whether they thought their beliefs were really sound.

Of course, there's a lot of overlap between these five different outcomes, but what they all added up to was the conclusion that reading began to plant the seeds of doubt in peoples' minds about what they'd always been told to accept. Books led to a step change in the way they now demanded *empirical facts*. Instead of simply having society's memes drilled into their heads by listening to others and then copying them, people now began to know more, to understand more, to think more for themselves, and to develop their own opinions and insights.

As literacy grew, so society became increasingly stratified. The beginnings of a professional class was now emerging with its own subdivisions and exams. Membership of professions such as the law and medicine mushroomed, academic scholarship increased, merchants were becoming wealthier and they, in turn, educated their children to climb the ladder and join the boss class.

With social levels now becoming more nuanced, certain trades like banking, brewing and colonial administraion were almost becoming acceptable occupations to the ruling elite. The *nouveaux* were certainly now splashing their *riche* around, much of it in the direction of royalty, and titles and advantageous marriages soon followed. Distinctions between the old gang of nobility, religious leaders and military bigwigs - and everyone else - became more muddled as important new roles and layers were introduced. In short, the period following the invention of printing saw a permanent resetting of the structure of society. Most significantly, perhaps, it saw the beginnings of the *middle class*.

The idea of education began to radically alter as well. Most written material before the 16th century had been in Latin, and books were scarce and knowledge was narrow. Now the notion was emerging that people could know far more than they ever had before. People were no longer regarding the owners of books as having godlike or even demonic powers, views that had been prevalent before because, as the American historian, Elizabeth Eisenstein, says in *The Printing Revolution in Early Modern Europe*: '… no human could possibly have access to that much information without divine intervention'.

As the prices of books fell, so the idea of academics belonging to a distinguished social class was established. Universities began to endow collections, and to appoint librarians who knew where different sources were kept. Scholars were now able to spend more time discussing their thoughts and writing to each other rather than searching for texts.

With extensive knowledge being held in a few major centres, original research became increasingly fashionable. And, with access to all this information, the previous belief that one could only accumulate wisdom with age began to be revised. It wasn't long before it was possible to be clever, learned and *youthful*, and recent graduates of the ancient universities began to be seen as citizens of value. The idea of young people having something worthwhile to say was taking root.

> **'Young minds provided with updated editions, especially of mathematical**
> **texts, began to surpass not only their elders but the wisdom of ancients as well.'**
> **Elizabeth Eisenstein, *The Printing Press as an Agent of Change***

So, where was the trouble coming from?

Well, it was the obverse of all this progress. Dangers were piling up as a result of the inevitable divergence of views that came with lots of different people reading - and the evidence that led to these opinions. The collective effect of all this was to spark an intellectual revolution that later became known as the Age of Enlightenment: a movement that came up from below in a natural manner, almost in the way that trading had originated. As with trade, it was another case of the right idea arising at the right time - without being micromanaged from above - and it was having a similarly widespread cultural impact.

Like most popular movements, it's difficult to say precisely when all the separate parts of it kicked off. What's not in much doubt, however, is that the new reading class was now leading to things being widely discussed in the fast-growing cities. As Robert Wright describes in *Nonzero*, the population densities of the larger trading centres were leading to increased levels of cooperation and trust. With this trend, he says, a separation was emerging between urban expectations and rural ones.

Contemporary Italian texts refer around this time to the country having 'good animals and bad men' while, in the larger towns, a momentum was growing that reason and scientific discoveries could overcome the myths and superstitions, religious dogma, and most of all, the blind obedience that had dominated people for centuries. Instead, there was now an opportunity for a fresh start; one in which human interaction would be based on a culture of idealism, toleration and rational thought. Wow.

This directional force was increasingly building to undermine the old order and the old certainties. Explosive ideas about things like individual liberty and the need for hard proof were questioning the teachings of the Church. More dangerous even than this, people were beginning to question the way that the monarchy's power was entwined with religion and the military. While this trinity might support each other, it was frequently standing in the way of what the common man wanted.

This was exciting stuff. There was even a growing interest in an old Greek idea called… democracy. Before long the social symbioses that had lasted for hundreds of years were coming under scrutiny in much the same way that the new-fangled microscopes were examining the natural world.

It all added up to Big Danger for the Big Men. The ordinary folk - people they'd have regarded as ingrates if they'd ever expressed a view - were now openly asking what the religious and governing classes were doing to deserve having their snouts so deep in the trough. Why, people were asking, should a few have so much and everyone else so little? These and other questions were now forming the seditious arguments in the mainstream of philosophical thought. Publishing might still have been in its infancy, but influential authors were beginning to emerge - and seeing their opinions consumed by huge numbers of people.

The cost of protest was plunging, and agitators were soon working out that they could easily send things to be published abroad to escape censorship. The pamphlet was the Twitter of its day, cheap, anonymous and quick to produce. In no time it became the hit-and-run instrument of political debate, and Europe's ruling class would have read them with mounting fury. If they'd actually stopped to think about their arguments, they must have realised that change was coming. The great majority of them did not: if you were born to rule, presumption and arrogance pretty well went with the territory.

Looking back to this time, we tend to think of the Renaissance as a time of artistic flowering and philosophical exploration. That may have been true in its first century, but it was movable type and mass communication that would prove to be the key factors in changing Europe. It was now moving from from a state of competitive patronage to its newfound passion for debate and discovery. Books and new ideas were shooting around in ways they'd never done before. Literacy was growing, the translation business was booming, and political argument was in fashion. The ground was shifting, and the direction it was taking was towards a permanent rearrangement of the structure of human societies.

'Literacy is the path from slavery to freedom. There are many kinds

of slavery and many kinds of freedom, but reading is still the path.'

Carl Sagan, *The Demon-Haunted World*

Elizabeth Eisenstein argues in her book *The Printing Press as an Agent of Change* that the deluge of information coming from publishers was fundamentally changing the mentality of mankind. Most importantly, she says, printing was the trigger that reversed the belief that there was only so much that could be known. Before this, no one had doubted that knowledge was finite and that the more that brainy people knew, the less there was to be discovered.

Now, just as mass printing had catalysed the spread of Renaissance thinking, so this new energy and its spirit of inquiry was leading to the Scientific Revolution and, from there, to the Age of Enlightenment. The more we knew, it was now becoming clear, the more this would show us what was yet to be discovered.

Scholars and scientists were becoming increasingly excited. Literacy and knowledge didn't lead to answers, they were saying, but to more questions. Religious theorists, physicists, philosophers, polymaths and everyone else who was rushing into print were working in collaboration with the new publishers and translators… and intellectual arrogance was rapidly becoming a thing of the past. The sea change in thinking was summed up in an appropriately maritime analogy from Sir Isaac Newton: 'What we know', he said, 'is a drop. What we don't know is an ocean.'

And what was the motor of all this change? It was nothing less than the logic of the market. People were voting with their hard cash: they were reading what interested them, and as the industry mushroomed, publishers were increasingly bringing out books that sold because they contained things that people wanted to hear. What were they? Lots of scholarly things, of course, but frequently they were anti-establishment, unregulated texts. These were the kinds of books that Briggs and Burke called 'dangerous reading', and monarchs and governments were now finding it almost impossible to stop them.

The religious authorities, in particular, were discovering that the cracks in their defensive walls were becoming so wide that they could no longer be papered over. Pressure on the Catholic Church during the Reformation went hand-in-hand with the spread of printing. Presses were being set up in foreign countries that were beyond a government's reach - Switzerland was a favourite - and a new trade was springing up to smuggle these rabble-rousing tracts across borders.

Just as leaders worry now about fake news and foreign interference on the internet, so then did the ruling class complain about exactly the same things. Books were spreading lies, they said, and corrupting the minds of stupid people - morons who were only too ready to lap up the sort of subversive thoughts and heresies that were being peddled by malcontents.

Stupid or not, the pressure grew. The Reformation questioned the Church; the Scientific Revolution questioned the ancient certainties and universal laws, and Enlightenment thinking was questioning what people could expect from their monarchs and rulers. Were the imbalances in society justifiable? Were the benefits being distributed fairly between the parties?

Of course not, howled back the underclass. The new information they were so readily lapping up was telling them there were better ways of doing things. Knowledge was kicking away the foundations of the old order, and the Age of Revolutions was underway.

**'The printing press is either the greatest blessing or the greatest
curse of modern times, sometimes one forgets which it is.'
Ernst Schumacher, *Small is Beautiful***

The English had by far the highest literacy rate in Europe by the middle of the 17th century and, to that extent, it's not surprising that they were the first out of the revolutionary starting stalls. What happened? Well, it all started when the king, Charles I, went into meltdown with his Parliament. The reason was that over a number of years, some basic questions had become ever more urgently in need of being answered. They were about nothing less than who called the shots in England. Who was actually in charge?

The King was in no doubt that he was. To some extent this was because he'd fallen into the same trap that so many celebrities do when they believe their own publicity. In Charles's case the reason the royal origin stories were lodged so deep in his psyche was because they were enshrined in English law as 'The Divine Right of Kings'. Where did this notion come from? From his own father no less, King James, who'd based his convictions on the matter as coming directly to him from the Bible.

Not thirty years before Charles was to have his showdown with Parliament, James had been very clear about the family's Big Man status when he'd written: '… for kings are not only God's lieutenants upon earth and sit upon God's throne, but even by

God himself they are called gods.' When the fight for supremacy then errupted, it wasn't simply a question of power that was being acted out, but the conviction that: '…whosoever therefore resisteth the power, resisteth the ordinance of God: and they that resist shall receive to themselves damnation.'

History has shown that rulers have always given themselves godlike qualities and Charles was no different. After all, hadn't he even been anointed with holy oils at his coronation, *ordaining* him as the monarch? What else could he do but think he was right? He and his supporters, the Royalists, all bought into the idea that if he derived his authority directly from God, then it could only mean one thing - that everyone else was wrong.

Since then, history and the movies have tended to romanticise the split between a top-down, unreconstructed absolutist monarchy (in which everyone wore pointy beards, vast white lace collars and feathered hats) and the grim faced, brutal looking Puritans (wearing the horrible steel helmets and unstylish leather jerkins of the New Model Army). The Royalists were for the old order of top-downers, and the Puritans billed themselves as representing the 'Mother of Parliaments', resolutely sticking up for the bottom-up rights of the little people. As ever, it was far more complicated than that.

In fact, Parliament in those days was made up of members of the gentry who were themselves all part of the ruling elite - and they'd only been selected by the King to rubber-stamp his demands for tax-raising rackets. But there'd been a falling out, and a long and complex series of events then took place that resulted in a horrific Civil War. Like all such internal conflicts, this one led to appalling levels of bloodshed - but it also resulted in the eventual resetting of the symbioses of society.

The role of the printing press in all this drama was, as Elizabeth Eisenstein was to later put it, the agent of change. England wasn't alone in seeing this. Access to published information was what would shape the modern world over the next three hundred years, and it was frequently the reason for the many other revolutions that would soon cascade down, one after the other.

Why were there so many of them? It was because they all seemed to conform to the same essential five-step process.

First, there'd be a complex and frequently confused series of events in which different shades of opinion would eventually clarify themselves into a binary choice. However much the people may have disliked reaching this point, the pressure of debate inevitably ended with them having to take one of only two sides. As ever, nuanced arguments are fine in the early stages, but we all know that revolutions occur when people are finally forced into deciding which side they're on. It's not so different now. Whatever your views might have been on Donald Trump and Joe Biden… in the end voters weighed it all up and just chose one or other of them.

Secondly, everyone gets sucked in. From the humblest to the most powerful in the land, what may have started as a limited row widens and widens until it includes the pent-up frustrations of an ever-growing number of people.

But, thirdly, the dispute is brought to the boil by the battle to win hearts and minds.

In the case of the lead-up to the English Civil War, the conflict might have been contained if it hadn't been for the new-found power of the printing press. By now agitators were using a welter of radical propaganda to stoke up animosity between the ruling layers and the common man. The weapon of choice for this was the pamphlet, and as male literacy levels in England were now well over thirty per cent, there were enough people to either read them silently, or to hear them shouted aloud in the alehouses.

Remarkably, Parliament had even recently passed a Bill for the Ordinance of Printing that followed a major push for freedom of speech and the lifting of censorship. Fatally for the Royalists this led, as Christopher Hill was to write in his great history of the period, *The World Turned Upside Down* to: '… a fantastic outburst of energy, both physical and intellectual… (from) the continuous flow of pamphlets on every subject under the sun. For a short time, ordinary people were freer from the authority of the Church and social superiors than ever before, or were for a long time to be again.'

Activists had also learned to raid the printers' type boxes for greater effect. The medium was definitely becoming the message, and pamphlets and posters were now using typefaces and font sizes that were designed to shriek out the underdog's rage.

Among the most vocal of these pamphleteers was the Puritan author of *Paradise Lost*, John Milton, whose eloquence and clarity of expression was whipping up dissent and reflecting the revolutionary fervour he heard around him. What did he want? A free press for 'God's Englishmen', he insisted, who weren't being permitted to say what they wanted to by the 'tyrannical duncery' of bishops. If the governing class continued in trying to stop them from making their legitimate complaints, he bellowed, there would be 'an undervaluing and vilifying of the whole nation.'

Terrible - but also untrue.

Fourthly is the cliché that every journalist and historian knows… that the first casualty of conflict is truth. Once the press was fired up, all bets were off. One of the major reasons for the hideous finale of the English Civil War, for example, was to be the long-running religious dispute in Ireland. Catholics, went the language of the pamphlets, were behaving horrifically towards Protestants.

Woodcut illustrations were doing the rounds that showed examples of the atrocities these violent zealots were supposedly guilty of. These caused opinion in England to become outraged, and the thirst for revenge soon reached a fever pitch. The only trouble was that these stories were almost certainly untrue. Engravings of previous vile actions were being recycled from earlier and completely unconnected wars on the Continent, but now with new captions stuck on them. Truth, as so often happens, went missing in the clamour for retribution.

But last, like all final revolutionary stages, there was a period of chaotic, group mental disturbance. As the symbiotic balance was being reset to greater democracy after a long period of suppression, so people became unmoored from the very certainties they were fighting so hard to pull down.

> 'Monarchy makes sense in a world where younger servants learn from older servants in a strict hierarchy. Once print made it possible to learn outside that hierarchy, the existence of privileged knowledge and even privilege itself could be called into question.'
> Diane Purkiss, *The English Civil War*

As Professor Hill describes it, the world truly becomes turned upside down at such a time. He recorded the English behaviour of the 1640s as people: '... speculated about the end of the world and the coming of the millennium; about the justice of God in condemning the mass of mankind to eternal torment for a sin which Adam committed; some of them became sceptical of the existence of hell. They contemplated the possibility that God might intend to save everybody, that something of God might be within each of us... they founded new sects to express these new ideas... they attacked the monopolisation of knowledge within the privileged professions, divinity, law, medicine... and proposed a vast expansion of educational opportunity. The eloquence, the power of the simple artisans who took place in these discussions was staggering.'

There were to be three quite separate civil wars between 1642 and 1651 and the first of these was won by the Parliamentarians. The country and the armies then waited to find out what would happen next. The leaders decided a new approach had to be thrashed out, and they met for a showdown at St Mary's Church in Putney, just over the river from where I live. They threw their hats on the altar and, for three days and three nights, debated the future of the country, arguing about how it should be governed - and, in particular, trying to reach a decision on whether the King should be executed.

Their passionate oratory was carefully transcribed, and among the records were the words of a man called Colonel Rainsborough, who so summed up the intention of their great revolution that his words remain still in the church today, painted on the wall over the entrance, a survivor of both time and fire.

'For really', he said, 'I think that the poorest hee that is in England hath a life to live, as the greatest hee...'

Incredible. Here, at last, was a ruling elite that recognised the claims of the people. From blood and sword, rulers had emerged who thought the underclass, the poor, the downtrodden and the have-nots, might have the right to a life. It was nothing less than the acceptance that each man had a voice, and that he should be listened to and even respected as an equal.

Slowly, England settled again as the madness of war passed. Charles may have lost his head but his sons were eventually recalled from exile and regime change led to a new bunch of entrants to the aristocracy. But things *had* changed - and they'd changed profoundly. Just as whole new life forms, genera and species, are unleashed in the natural world by catastrophe and extinction, so revolutions are frequently followed by periods of great creativity in which there are enormous leaps forward in society's cultural evolution. Whether Stephen Jay Gould is right or wrong about genetic variation, it's certainly true that the 'jerk' thesis can be seen to operate in our own development as a social species.

It didn't slow down from this point either. The tide of knowledge wouldn't be stopped, and roughly a hundred years after the English had fought themselves to a bloody restart, people in their American colony decided that they, too, had had enough of their symbiotic relationship - this time with the mother country. Again, the parties disagreed about the balance of benefits, and again it took a revolution to resolve it.

'The press is not only free, it is powerful. That power is ours. It is the proudest that man can enjoy. It was not granted by monarchs, it was not gained by aristocracies; but it sprang from the people and, with an immortal instinct, it has always worked for the people.'

Benjamin Disraeli, *The Vindication of the English Constitution*

As in England, the emerging print culture played a huge part in giving voice to the slew of perceived injustices. One of the most passionate writers was a revolutionary called Tom Paine, who'd crossed the Atlantic to add his skills as a mass communicator. He was a genius at expressing the idea of freedom, and the need for people to care enough about their liberty to be prepared to sacrifice their lives for it.

The printing presses went into overdrive as he produced a series of astonishingly effective pamphlets. One of them, *Common Sense*, was so successful that half a million copies were produced. Compared to the literacy levels of the time, this kind of circulation suggests it was consumed by ten times the number of people, relative to the size of the population, that read the *Harry Potter* publishing phenomenon of our own day.

George Washington realised just what power the written word could have. Before major engagements he would have the opening paragraphs of one of Paine's other pamphlets, *The American Crisis*, read to his waiting army:

'These are the times that try men's souls. The summer soldier and the sunshine patriot will, in this crisis, shrink from the service of his country; but he that stands it now, deserves the love and thanks of man and woman. Tyranny, like Hell, is not easily conquered; yet we have this consolation with us, that the harder the conflict, the more glorious the triumph.' Fantastic stuff… hand me a musket.

Across the Atlantic, the French looked on and were inspired. Their relationship with their own, egregious ruling class was particularly strained. 'L'etat, c'est moi' said Louis XIV referring to the royal family's ownership of pretty much everything in the country. And the people shouted back at a later Louis: '… no, it isn't. And why don't you step this way to the guillotine, monsieur?'

What had got them going? Among other things, the country's intellectuals had been continuously whipped up into a fine froth over the previous twenty years by a periodical called *L'Encyclopedie*, that set out to use radical articles to inform and even to change the way that people thought. It was edited by a maverick philosopher called Dennis Diderot, and he employed a number of rock star writers that included Voltaire, Montesquieu and Rousseau. His intention was to publish an encyclopaedia of the world's knowledge - but in a secular, anti-Jesuitical way.

At that time Paris was the intellectual capital of Europe and the publication was attracting a reasonable readership… until the authorities made the mistake of banning it in 1759. At that point it went underground, printed over the Swiss border and, of course, it now became required reading by anyone who wanted to be thought of as *au courant*.

Not for the first time, and certainly not for the last, the authorities had been deluding themselves if they thought information could be prevented from reaching the people. Instead of this happening, its influence grew with the appearance of every one of its 72,000 articles and, as it did, so the general view increased that the social unfairness in the country would have to be addressed.

Perhaps more than anything else, the *Encyclopedie* explored the relationship between the individual and the state. Intellectual liberalism was rife, and even French aristocrats began to flirt with revolutionary ideas. Diderot went back to first principles and asked - what did people really want? What was the 'general will'? Possibly more importantly, what was humanity's *natural* state before 'civilisation' changed him? Set against this, what was society's responsibility to produce laws that would benefit everyone?

Following the same pattern that England had witnessed, the spark that would throw France into revolution was a financial crisis. The country managed to narrowly avoid bankruptcy, but a tipping point had now passed and the French descended precipitously into the five stages of revolution that the horrified English had seen unfold. First, the binary choice: would one come down on the side of the monarchy and its *ancien regime* - or be against them?

Next, came the compulsion to join in, to no longer be able to shrug and blow one's cheeks out in a resigned manner at the ways of the world. Now one had to have an opinion, even to pick up a weapon.

Then came the propaganda battle and with it an avalanche of pamphlets.

Fourth was the fading of certainty, of knowing what to believe in, and of truth and social cohesion. As WB Yeats was to later write in *The Second Coming* about the similarly frenzied atmosphere after the First World War: 'The best lack all conviction, while the worst are full of passionate intensity.'

And, last, like a volcano erupting came the mental disturbance, the fire and slaughter, the hideous chaos of the Jacobins, the mob, the riots, the Reign of Terror, the lethal intrigues, the explosion of weird religious sects, the score settling and the final meltdown of bloodletting with its 40,000 executions and murders.

> **'The people may kill, burn, ravage, commit the most frightening cruelties,**
> **glorify the hero today and throw him in the gutter tomorrow, it is all the same.**
> **Gustave Le Bon, *The Psychology of Revolution***

As in England, the fever eventually lifted, and with this came the emergence of a clear leader. Like a nightclub bouncer wading into an exhausted pile of drunken scrappers, a military genius went from cadet to Emperor in a hundred months, thirty-eight of them spent away on unofficial leave in Corsica. The young man was Napoleon, and in 1799 he came to power and the pendulum swung back: first to order, and then to creativity, liberality of expression and patriotism.

Yet under his new political regime, the clarity of direction was a written one that could be printed and distributed. It was a political code, a new kind of stated authority, and its intention was to enshrine the fresh start to the social symbiosis between the people and their rulers. Equality before the law, the dismantling of feudalism, elected administrators and a transparent legal system were all now part of the new agreement.

Although this written constitution might have been produced in a crazy rush, it was to give the world its reset button. As the idea of re-examining the interests of different layers in societies took hold, revolutions elsewhere embraced Napoleon's constitutional code, and its influence spread across the globe. Now one nation after another demanded a more equitable sharing of society's benefits.

Had the printing press been part of this eruption? Well, put it this way, when France's jails were stormed and emptied of political prisoners by the Revolution, there were over eight hundred printers, authors and publishers behind their high walls. It was a picture that was to be repeated in other places. Knowledge and information are toxic for strongmen and then, as now, the press was very much fuel to the fire.

Who came after the French? The race was on… reform or revolution. In Spain the *illustrados*, or 'enlightened spirits' looked at their neighbour's upheaval and led their government into an alliance with Napoleon against the British. In Germany there was a recasting of the political landscape. Many of its radicals had gone to Paris but had become disillusioned with the 'terror' and preferred, instead, to push for moderation rather than rampant violence.

Many others throughout Europe looked over the Atlantic at what had happened in America. They saw events there as being more relevant, less bloody and more practical than the French. The American emphasis on the constitution, the federal system, individual rights, religious toleration, and the rule of law all led to a reshaping of political mindsets.

Next were the upheavals of foreign colonies as they, too, demanded their independence. South America became a site of radicalism with many Europeans fighting in Bolivar's legions, the Uruguayan war of independence, and in the two Brazilian uprisings. In Haiti there was a slave revolt - the only one that would ever ultimately lead to the establishment of a new state. This particularly shook the French, as Haiti had provided them with over a third of their overseas trade and revenue.

Rebellions and upheavals followed in Portugal, Italy and Greece and then, ultimately, with the national unification movements in Italy, Germany, Hungary and Poland.

Some countries hung on to the old ways. In Russia the ancient system of serfdom ran so deep in the collective psyche that the 'Big Man versus the rest' system would last for another hundred years until the revolution of 1917. The First World War had started three years earlier as the pressures in societies, and between competing countries, had built to intolerable levels.

This war marked another watershed in which the headlong changes brought by mechanisation, manufacturing and communication were colliding with largely agrarian societies where little had changed for generations. The car and the railway were having an enormous impact on communities where people had previously rarely travelled, the telephone revolutionised communication for societies used to the messenger and the mail, literacy had risen everywhere and national newspapers were now doing the job of a million village pumps.

Of course, the biggest change of all was the gradual introduction of universal suffrage. At last, the way that social symbioses worked could be voted on. Profound rebalancing became possible; and women, in particular, began their long haul back to the egalitarianism they'd last seen in hunter-gatherer societies.

> '**A social movement that only moves people is merely a revolt.**
> **A movement that changes both people and institutions is a revolution.**'
> Martin Luther King Jr., *Why We Can't Wait*

The First War was to prove to be the start of a seventy-five year period during which the world was almost never at peace. From 1914 to the fall of the Berlin Wall and the collapse of Communism in 1989, there were virtuously continuous conflicts breaking out as differing ideologies, racism, suffrage, the profound wish of people for independence and social justice, and a dozen other reasons reshaped the political landscape.

As long as freedom of expression could continue, then never again would authority go unquestioned. One would have thought that the age of Big Men was coming to an end, yet almost incredibly there are some that remain to this day. But the notions of fairness, of equality, of human rights, of cooperation and of the sharing of the benefits of society were now deeply established. These became our new memes, and they were not to be reversed. Knowledge really is power, and once humans were allowed information in their lives, then cultural evolution accelerated.

But if these were the stages of our history, then what did the political thinkers and lawmakers that came after the great revolutions conclude were the best *governance systems*? Few would have disagreed that societies needed some kind of order to make them function efficiently. But if the symbioses that operated throughout society were being shaken up and reworked, then what did people feel should come once the process of readjustment had started?

'They asked me what kind of service I wanted and
I insisted it shouldn't be too flashy.'

THE ARGUMENT THAT THE ACQUISITION OF KNOWLEDGE SHOULD BE LISTED AS OUR SEVENTH GREAT REVOLUTION IS BASED ON THE BELIEF THAT IT ALLOWED PEOPLE TO INFLUENCE THE RELATIONSHIP BETWEEN THE RULED AND THEIR RULERS. THE OLD MODEL FOR THE SYMBIOSES IN HUMAN SOCIETIES WAS OVER. BUT WHAT WAS TO TAKE ITS PLACE?

In February 1972, Richard 'I am not a crook' Nixon finally pulled off one of his long-held foreign policy ambitions when he managed to reopen diplomatic relations with China. For a second time the country had allowed itself to become isolated from the outside world - this time due to of the hardline edicts of the Cultural Revolution - and it was now prepared to come in from the cold.

In an exact repeat of its withdrawal from the world five hundred years earlier, the Communist leaders had decided that they, just as the emperors had before them, regarded the influence of outside ideas as too much of a threat.

Now a tour had been arranged and the dangerous Yankees were coming to see things for themselves. The background to this thawing of relations had been due, of all things, to a resumption of ping pong matches between the two nations. But this tiny crack was to soon open up into a far wider opportunity. Terms and negotiations for the trip had gone backwards and forwards, but eventually an excited Nixon set off on what he was to label, with his characteristic modesty, as: 'the week that changed the world.'

As ever, he had at his side his equally enthusiastic Secretary of State, a superstar mover and shaker and self-styled peacenik called Henry Kissinger. Kissinger might have been a heavyweight global figure, but he wasn't everyone's cup of tea. Among lighter criticisms, some regarded him as a world-class bore, best known for handing out his ponderously expressed geopolitical insights.

Once the American party had arrived, Kissinger employed his usual *weltanschauung* oratory to make small talk with the Chinese premier, Zhou Enlai. Unsurprisingly, it proved to be a struggle, and he consistently found it hard to find common ground until, one day in the kick around before a meeting started, the master diplomat asked Zhou about the time the old survivor had spent as a student in Paris.

Kissinger ended by enquiring in his heavy German accent what Zhou thought the influence had been of the French Revolution. Apparently, Zhou pondered deeply when the interpreter had finished speaking, and then replied:

'Too soon to say.'

How everyone laughed. The media had a field day of it, comparing the Chinese way of measuring human progress in generations, while Nixon's horizon went no further than the re-election campaign he was cranking up for a second term later that year. This reaction led the Chinese to bridle at what they regarded as patronising coverage, and they soon hit back by claiming that Zhou had misunderstood the question.

But should they have bothered with the backtrack? Many people felt they shouldn't and that they would have been better off sticking to the interesting argument that the profound reboots unleashed by the Age of Revolutions were, in reality, still in their infancy.

After all, only a couple of hundred years or so had elapsed since the French rose up in 1789. Set against that, there'd been millions before it during which the great majority of humans had spent their lives locked in ludicrously unfair relationships with their rulers.

Ever since our species had begun to develop into something we'd recognise today - and had then started organising itself into hunter-gatherer tribes - societies had been shoved around by a tiny number of selfish Big Men who saw their job as telling everyone what to think and do. In their presumptuously superior minds, they'd always seen themselves as the queens of the human hive, with the ordinary folk as just the disposable worker bees.

> '**Unless you do everything for liberty, you have done nothing. There are no**
> **two ways of being free: one must be entirely free, or become a slave once more.**'
> **Maximillien Robespierre, *Virtue and Terror***

Can you really blame them though? Humans have always shown a capacity for zero sum strategies, even for extreme self-centeredness, and strong leaders would have argued that without their firm hand controlling a bunch of competitive personalities, our brute impulses would always threaten the well-being of communities. Yes, people might say, the boss class had often taken too big a bite out of society's pie… but surely *someone* had to lay down the law?

Trade changed all that. Trade allowed the non-zero sum side of our natures to emulate the cooperative strategies that are so apparent in other organisms. After all, colonies in the natural world have group structures and survival mechanisms that arrive at balance and self-organising stability… without the need for law and order. If they can manage it, why can't we?

In that sense, our instinct for trading was arguably the most important of the bottom-up processes. It owed nothing to the edicts and strictures of rulers. But did things really change that much when specialisation and exchange came along? Yes, without question they did, and if one takes the really long view of our cultural evolution, then it's pretty obvious that from the point at which trading outside the tribal community took off, the Big Man's status was always bound to weaken.

Naturally, the ruling class did everything they could to hold things back. But when the Age of Revolutions began to shake up the world order, the role of monarchs and other Big Men came under the kind of scrutiny they'd become used to handing out to others. This was greatly accelerated when our wish to find fair ways of dividing benefits was enlarged by the 'brain outside the brain' of numbers and written records - and then, of course, as the impact of the printing press took hold.

At this point the growth of non-zero cooperation took on an unstoppable momentum of its own. And it worked best when people were physically close to each other, something that meant the greatest progress was usually seen in urban communities. That's because the more that people could talk and share information, the more behavioural memes and social gains could spread. The sparser populations of rural areas held them back.

It wasn't all plain sailing though. People might have welcomed the idea of the old suppressions being reviewed… but gaining one's freedom by sloughing off the Big Man's hand wasn't always without pain. 'Bliss it was that dawn to be alive…', Thomas Carlyle would say about the French Revolution (and who doesn't enjoy watching the rulers' applecart being overturned?) but history tends to repeat itself in showing there's a high price to be paid for the entertainment.

The first problem arises because the ruling class is almost invariably replaced by an even nastier bunch. Not only would these new bosses be awash in revolutionary hatred and thirst for revenge, but they'd also lack any experience when it came to pulling the levers of power. Almost invariably this made them inept at the job of running a government. Yet however vicious they were, it never seems to have occurred to them that this could ever have anything to do with their own shortcomings.

But, secondly, whenever there's a social upheaval, most ordinary people rapidly come to the uncomfortable realisation that it's easier to know what they *don't* want, rather than what they *do*. We might resent the strings of authority when they're yanking us around like a puppet, yet when a big pair of revolutionary scissors comes along to cut them, it can be a shock to find ourselves left in an uncertain heap.

'We need a government, alas, because of the nature of humans.'
PJ O'Rourke, *Republican Party Reptile*

The natural world, of course, doesn't have this problem. Mutational evolution means that organisms sometimes have to find new partners for symbiotic relationships, but forced changes settle down over the immeasurably long periods of evolutionary time. And when they do, the deal never changes.

In other words, once symbioses are in place then there are no later renegotiations of the benefits. The vast majority of organisms are stuck with their arrangements until mutations lead to gene changes that are passed down vertically through the generations, something that happens over colossal periods of time. The exception to this rule are the prokaryotes, who are able to make rapid changes through Horizontal Gene Transfer.

We humans do change however… and we change fast. We can alter the way we behave with other people in seconds. We hop around as we react to others, changing our minds in a flash if we think there's an advantage to be made, giving out one lot of signals and then, just as quickly, sending out another. This might all add up to be a tremendous asset as being nimble and prescient is useful for surviving challenges. But it certainly makes us tricky to read - and deeply elusive as relieable partners.

This ability of ours to change so quickly is also at the root of much unhappiness. Our massive brains are being put to good use when we weigh up situations and arrive at our behavioural choices, but we're frequently overriding our genetic and biological drives when we decide what to do. The conflict that ensues then frequently makes us suffer because, as ever, serving two masters leads to painful consequences.

We make things even more difficult for ourselves by having a further kink in our make-ups. This is the trick that allows us to hold two quite contradictory views in our heads at the same time. This might allow us to navigate all manner of complicated situations, yet the strain often leaves us confused and unsettled.

Nietzsche made a career out of banging on about this problem, and in insisting that we should recognise the self-authority we have over our lives. He called this 'the will to power', and while it made him a figure of philosophical importance, it also ended up sending him off his rocker.

Watching a shepherd once casually butchering a flock of sheep by slitting their throats, he summed up his view of the conflict: 'Will, pure will! Without the problems and complexities of intellect - what freedom!' Freedom it may have seemed in his book, but experience tells us that ignoring the complexity of our thought processes - and our unconscious drives - is easier to write about than to practice.

While it may be true that too much Nietzschean forcefulness can undermine our equilibrium, the history of mass information triggering rebellions and revolutions shows that sudden liberty can be tough on the human psyche. This means that for many of us, it's easier to grumble about the imposed certainties of rulers than to create our own philosophies for living.

The period of the English Civil War was a good example of this. The twin pillars of the monarchy and religion might have been pulled down - but what was going to be erected in their place? In the desperate search for direction, the vacuum was filled by an onrush of religious denominations that conflated Christian beliefs with social justice.

The Levellers, for example, followed a creed that preached an overarching message of tolerance and equality. The Diggers rejected property rights and believed in grabbing land for communal ownership. The Quakers saw others as friends, and thought everyone should quake in their direct relationship with God's directing hand. The Seekers believed we would find the right path by using the power of silence, while the pantheistic Ranters ranted about their denial of religious authority - and insisted that humans could only make progress if everyone went around naked.

These were just a few of the reasonably sensible new sects. Then there were those on the freaky fringes like the Muggletonians, who were hostile to human hypotheses and based their scriptural understanding on cosmology; and the Fifth Monarchy Men with their conviction that the prophetic dream of Nebuchadnezzar in the Book of Daniel would point humanity towards paradise.

Sub-sects like the Swedenborgians broke away from their mother churches, and tiny local communities such as the Grindletonians became passionate followers of a charismatic leader. Last, a whole slew of nonconformist faiths would continue to influence where we are going, leading eventually to sects like the wonderfully named Walworth Jumpers, whose delirious adherents danced ecstatically as they waited for the Second Coming.

Some of these spiritual solutions faded away, and might now seem mildly baffling from the distant viewpoint we have today. But however odd their reasoning now appears, their followers agreed on one big principle… if there wasn't going to be a king to tell them what to do, then *something else* had to replace him if societies were to be governed.

But what?

What, in particular, was to be done about establishing an ultimate authority that would sit in judgement above us all? Who would elect the layers of people needed to administer the rules they thought were needed to hold back the selfish forces that humans were prey to? Monarchs might have taken too much… but someone now had to tell the man in the street what he could and couldn't do.

Pre-revolutionary populations had also become indoctrinated by living in monarchical societies. They'd been in these relationships for such a long time that they found it difficult to imagine who or what could replace the order they'd imposed. Kings were what everyone was used to, and people were reluctant to give them up.

When Charles I was executed, for instance, people generally thought another monarch would take over in his place. Cromwell titled himself 'Lord Protector', and while he may have personally kept his feet on the ground, demanding that his portrait be painted 'warts and all', the moment he was dead the governing class even considered offering to crown his son, Richard, and so initiate a new royal dynasty in his name.

Washington, too, had to reject numerous requests for him to become America's monarch. Other countries simply filled a void by recruiting someone they particularly admired, even though he might be a foreigner. Napoleon, being Napoleon, showed little truck for such modesty and had himself named Emperor. He then followed this up by shamelessly giving the thrones of all the places he'd conquered to his brothers.

But if the balance of benefits between the monarchs and the underclass were to be reset - how should this be done? The presumption and corruption of absolute rulers might be coming to an end, but if they were no longer going to impose their version of order on society, then what was a better model?

Pretty quickly the penny was dropping that solving this issue wasn't just about finding a new rule book for the *leaders* - it was also critical that their *followers* knew what was expected of them. This was urgently needed because post-revolutionary societies were now witnessing the early glimmerings of political machinations, and of embryonic representative democracy. Along with these went the notion of pluralism, an important novelty, because if the philosophies of government and political parties were taking their first tentative steps, then the concept of having opposing views was part and parcel of the new landscape.

Debating what the next stages should be now became a hot topic. How were people going to agree what the balance of interests should be between the new rulers and what the 'poorest hees in the land' would regard as fair?

Once again, the English took the lead. They'd chopped the head off their king and then they'd laid down the terms under which his two sons could return to the country. This Restoration, began well enough as the elder of the brothers - Charles II - turned out to be nimbly evasive as he handled power. But when he died without leaving a legitimate heir, and his brother James inherited the crown, the new king arrogantly began to return to the old 'do as I say, or else' ways.

> **'Apart from heredity monarchy, there was not much in which Charles believed in this world or another. He wanted to be king as was his right and have a pleasant life. He was cynical rather than cruel, and indifferent rather than intolerant.**
> **Winston Churchill, *A History of the English Speaking People***

The major issue the new king refused to compromise on was religion. He was a staunch Catholic in what was by now a Protestant country, and his belief in his own authority became so unyielding that, in the end, the English decided he had to go. Did they execute him as well? No, surprisingly not. Instead there was a peaceful uprising, and rarely for an overthrow, violence wasn't used. Rather, the King was simply presented with an ultimatum: since he no longer had the confidence of the nation, there was the door.

And so he took it, departing into exile in France, and being replaced on the throne by his daughter and her Protestant Dutch husband. This extraordinary upheaval rejoices in the name of the Glorious Revolution, and its impact on society's progress can hardly be overstated… because if ordinary men and women could rise up and throw out a king, then that was real people power. Suddenly, anything was possible.

The seat of ultimate authority had shifted and it was never going to go back. The seeds of self-determination had been planted. And, around the world, governments began to face up to the issue of deciding how society would be structured - and how to act in the best interests of its citizens.

Yet how should this be done? The great men thought and argued, and the idea of a *social contract* was born - the essential belief that people would only ever live together in harmony if they could agree to a number of moral and political rules of behaviour… and what the deal would be between the ruling elite and the common man. These agreements, they said, could either be written down as laws, or they might simply become recognised as general standards by which any civilised society would acknowledge and follow.

But what was right and wrong about mankind if the contract was going to be fair? And how could such an arrangement be monitored once it was in place?

"Are you sure everyone will know we're being ironic?"

Now we were getting to the crunchy bits, because at the heart of the many different theories to emerge were the terms for new symbioses, and therefore for a rebalancing of the social benefits. In short, any deal would be based on an individual recognising that he'd be giving up a certain degree of liberty if he followed society's rules… even if he didn't like them.

In return, the state would protect his 'rights' to things like property, freedom of expression, enforceable legal agreements, and a natural expectation to a good life within a peaceful and law-abiding social order.

But what was the 'state' anyway? Ah, people were pretty much in agreement on that. If the state was to be the fundamental unit of control, they said, then it had to be an institution that *deserved* its peoples' respect and loyalty. The idea of justice was to be key to this respect, because fair laws had to demand reciprocal obedience. Unjust ones did not.

So far, so good, but the next hurdle was then the question of what people were *really* like. If you could understand them and their compulsions, went the argument, then you could design a state to fit their needs. This was the way that social agreements could more fairly share out the symbiotic benefits so they suited everyone.

So who was going to say how this social contract should be balanced?

What were the responsibilities of each of the parties going to be - and how much would each of them have to compromise to find something that made sense... for as many people as possible?

The Social Contract made flesh... the king is
made of people, and people make the king.

CHAPTER SEVENTEEN

IF HUMANS WERE ABLE TO USE THEIR COLLECTIVE GENIUS TO COME UP WITH BETTER SYMBIOTIC RELATIONSHIPS BETWEEN THE DIFFERENT INTERESTS IN SOCIETY - THEN WHAT WAS IT GOING TO BE? AND HOW WOULD ARRIVING AT THIS PROCESS AVOID CHAOTIC UPHEAVALS?

One of the major figures that stepped forward to try and square the circle of social contract theory - and so influence the way that governments should be structured - was a brilliant mathematician called Thomas Hobbes. He'd risen through his powerful contacts to become a highly regarded influence in the new world that was being shaped, yet he was already sixty-three in 1651 when he set down his beliefs in a great work of political insight called *Leviathan*.

Who was he? And, why was he so important? Well, like so many others, the clues are in his background. Born prematurely in Wiltshire in 1588, his mother had gone into labour with the shock of being told that the Spanish Armada was sailing up the Channel. Hobbes was later to enjoy saying that she'd given birth to twins: 'myself and fear', but many people since then came to regard this as a fairly dusty joke because his entire world view was shaped by just that... fear.

After an extensive education he'd become a tutor and companion to a number of aristocrats. He had then joined the rush of people that moved to Paris as the English Civil War became inevitable. Hobbes was to stay there for the next eleven years, sharing his exile with the Royal Stuarts, and it wasn't long before he'd been approached to take up the position of mathematical instructor to the young Prince Charles - the man who'd return later to England as Charles II. It's tempting to say that any understanding of Hobbes's philosophy of government was largely shaped by this relationship.

Like many academics and thinkers, Hobbes's thinking was influenced by the giants of the Scientific Revolution. He'd read widely, and had developed the belief that we humans and everything else on earth might be complicated organic bodies, but that at base we were all just matter in constant motion, interacting with each other under universal laws of nature. Sounds a lot like a description of our molecular structures, really.

He rejected the idea that humans were any different to other organisms, and he thought instead that nothing about us could ever be described as either wholly 'good' or 'bad'. His view was that we were like the rest of the natural world in that our survival drives made us understandably self-absorbed.

Our outlooks, he thought, would therefore be moulded by wanting to look after ourselves. Not too bad a conclusion, you might think. But he then went further than that - and for many people rather too far - when he made his most famous claim that without a strong hand to control us, and without a social contract that would constrain our drives, we humans would quickly descend into the same State of Nature in which every other organism was living.

And this, in his view, was *omnium bellum contra omnes* - 'a war of all against all'. In other words, we would become like everything else in life and find ourselves in a constant state of conflict in which we were consuming each other in a desperate bid to stay alive. What this implied, he said, was that we'd all be incentivised to kill or subjugate those around us if we weren't being held in check by the 'Terrour of some Power'. By this he meant that unless we were *fearful* of being punished by authority for the way we behaved, our natural state was to be endlessly at one another's throats.

It was fear, according to Hobbes, that was the only thing we'd all understand. If we were always in dread of people rubbing us out, then any social contract had to guarantee us protection and security if we were to reciprocate our individual rights - as long as others could be made to give up theirs too. How to do this? With a big stick, he said, something like the biblical sea monster that Job describes as an instrument of God's supreme control over suffering and evil... a *Leviathan*.

If we didn't do that, the most widely quoted passage in his book booms out, we'd all be in a state of perpetual war with each other in which there'd be no basis for society and: '... worst of all, continual fear, danger of violent death; and the life of man, solitary, poor, *nasty, brutish and short.*'

Pretty gloomy stuff. But who could blame him for thinking this way? The Civil War in England had just killed over 200,000 people - a grotesque number, and roughly the equivalent of three million if one equated it to today's population size. No wonder he thought humans were unspeakable, deranged monsters.

For him, a grand bargain for society was the only way to keep all the parties under control. But how was a social contract in which cooperation was key, promises were kept, laws were followed and one's property was protected, going to be enforced? The only way was to have a *Leviathan* in charge, Hobbes said, an absolute authority that would be a strong enforcement mechanism… someone, in other words, that looked remarkably like a sovereign.

It's hard not to think that Hobbes wasn't rather biassed in his thinking. He knew the Stuarts well, he'd been protected by them, helped with their restoration to the monarchy and so on. Nonetheless, he also knew that things had moved on in the world, and that the old ways of doing things were over.

He therefore set himself against the principle of the Divine Right of Kings. In his view, God and religions had no part to play in arriving at a legitimate authority. Nor did he see a future for the layers of corrupt aristocrats who'd had their spoons in the soup for so long.

Instead, Hobbes was utterly convinced that it was only the threat of punishment that would keep people in a state of 'fairness' with one another. To ensure this happened, an absolute power should have the right to rule over people's lives. He could even act harshly if he had to - do anything, in fact, to *keep order*.

'To this war of every man against every man, this also in consequent; that nothing can be unjust. The notions of right and wrong, justice and injustice have there no place. Where there is no common power, there is no law, where no law, no injustice. Force, and fraud, are in war the cardinal virtues.'
Thomas Hobbes, *Leviathan*

No king from now on, the book exclaimed, could or should be rich while his subjects went poor. Similarly, no society could ever be successful unless its peoples were governed in a way that acted in their best interests. That was how social symbioses could work and, to illustrate the principle, *Leviathan* had a cover illustration that became a metaphor for his core ideas. On it, the crowned figure of the monarch is carefully depicted as constructed of a mass of his tiny subjects. The king, Hobbes was clearly saying, was the people. And the people made their king. It was a deal.

Hobbes's thinking was to have a huge influence on how the world's new societies and their politics were being formed. Yet many people still took issue with his underlying view of human nature. Were we really so terrible if we were reduced down to our natural state, they asked? As memories of the Civil War receded, other thinkers began to imagine that humans might not be quite as bad as Hobbes had painted them. And it was at this point that a new superbrain stepped forward to offer an alternative point of view.

The man's name was John Locke and he'd been an undergraduate when *Leviathan* had first appeared. Like Hobbes he'd come from a modest background, and again like him, he'd initially become distinguished by his career as a brilliant scholar. Instead of mathematics, though, Locke had gone on to become a notable physician, and his great skills had attracted a number of Britain's richest and most important aristocrats to become patients and patrons. As they'd listened to him talk, many of them had become increasingly intrigued by his views on social contract theory, and they began to encourage and sponsor him to set his ideas down in print.

When he did this, and the four books that made up his *Essay Concerning Human Understanding* first came out in 1689, it was quickly apparent that where his vision of humanity most departed from Hobbes's thinking was in the way he imagined what our 'State of Nature' was. What had we been like at the time of our origins? This was critical because, just as Hobbes had, he saw the basis of a fair society as a return to the equalities of a purer, more innocent age.

In our natural state, Locke claimed, men and women had lived in complete liberty, running their lives as they saw fit, and not bothering with trying to control other people. And, like many others, Locke thought that the Glorious Revolution had shown that there were more peaceful ways of provoking beneficial social change than by using violence and warfare.

Instead of this, he said, civil society was an opportunity for ordinary people to resolve their conflicts with the *help* of the government. In his vision, any social contract should meet a citizen's key demand for having his property and other rights protected. It was the state's primary duty, therefore, to structure laws around how we could live with this security in place, but without the interference of others.

The people's side of the deal, he went on, was that we would have the responsibility to act morally, and to behave considerately to others. Yes, one had individual rights, but equally everyone had to be subject to the *will of the majority*. In his view, if the king, or the government, or even society let the individual down, and people weren't protected, then ordinary citizens had the right to rise up and take the law into their own hands.

> 'Men being, as has been said, all free, equal and independent, no one can be put out of this estate, and subjected to the political power of another, without his own consent.'
> John Locke, *Second Treatise of Government*

Well, if anyone could be said to have pulled the philosophical trigger for the subsequent worldwide revolutions, it was Locke. To the nascent Whig party in England, he was a hero. Widely read in Britain, he became the embodiment of Enlightenment values to political philosophers everywhere, a proponent of limited government, of toleration, and of reason.

Admired by Voltaire in France, and also by the angst-ridden German theorists, his theories crossed the Atlantic to become central to the thinking of Alexander Hamilton and Thomas Jefferson. In one of the most famous passages in his essays, Locke had spoken of the need to preserve 'life, liberty (and) estate', to which the Declaration of Independence would later add '… and the pursuit of Happiness' to its list of inalienable rights.

On the other side of the Channel, the writers of *L'Encyclopedie* took note of Locke's views and pondered deeply. Pretty well everyone agreed that something had to be done about the unacceptable lack of representation in France, yet the governing class responded by putting their heads ever deeper in the sand.

Among the most influential of the people pushing back at this wilful blindness wasn't actually French at all, but Swiss. His name was Jean-Jacques Rousseau, and he was a strange and difficult man from Geneva, who'd made a reasonable living as a musical theorist but who now seemed intent on getting his revenge for the childhood rejection he believed he'd suffered. He was attracting a lot of attention and his ideas now began to chime with others about what a fair social contract should look like… even if getting to it might involve a few stages of violent upheaval, or even slaughter.

Like Hobbes and Locke before him, Rousseau also viewed society through the prism of how Man would have lived in a State of Nature. What was he essentially like, in other words, before the complexities of life had buggered him up? Unlike the others though, Rousseau's romantic vision was that we'd all begun as Noble Savages: peaceful, non-competitive, morally pure, and endlessly compassionate.

Our journey into modern life, he insisted, had been dominated by unfair and cruel Big Men, and it was their vile treatment of us that had corrupted mankind away from its natural innocence - a purer, freer way of living that was still to be observed,

Rousseau said, in the primitive tribes left in the world. His rose tinted specs were so seductive, in fact, that people fell over themselves to agree with his idyllic views, even going so far as to travel overseas to witness the paragons for themselves.

Robert Wright relates in *Nonzero*, however, how early travellers to French Polynesia were more than mildly disappointed when they saw that instead of the tribes being peaceable hippies living in harmony, there was actually almost continuous warfare going on between them. Visions of their fabled innocence and nobility, he says, were understandably shaken at the sight of victorious chieftains pounding the corpses of their enemies to make them flat enough to be worn as trophy cloaks.

In spite of these and other rumours, Rousseau wasn't to be deflected, and in his most quoted phrase he claimed that: 'man was born free, yet everywhere he is in chains'. Good turn of phrase - but just plain wrong. He was never free: he'd always been subject to an order-giving hierarchy, and the iron hand of Big Men who'd directed his movements. Just as Hobbes and Locke had before him, Rousseau was shooting in the dark.

Why had they all so misunderstood our origins? Well, first, none of the three would have had a clue about the genetic or biological steps that had led to *H. sapiens'* evolution. Nor, secondly, could they ever have imagined the role of the gene, or the historical transmissions and cultural revolutions that we'd been shaped by.

Besides these, though, they'd also have had little recognition of the endless interplay between the conflict and cooperation choices in the behaviour of living things.

And, lastly, they would have had no knowledge of the Laws of Thermodynamics that were making these two survival strategies so continuously interlinked, and yet so complementary.

Yet when these and the other great philosophers of the time were turning their hypotheses into theories on social fairness, they were all assuming that mankind's inner drive was to return to an unsullied State of Nature.

> 'Call it what you will: Eden, Arcadia, the Golden Age, the primaeval innocence.
> It is the idyllic state of affairs that lies at the root of all human imagination. All
> poetry and all music, and all art, actually, testify to the inconsolable yearning in
> us to recover that state; or at least to glimpse it; or at least... to mourn it.'
> **Thomas Howard,** *Dove Descending*

Without the insights we have now, however, they had no concept of how cooperative activities had developed in humans, nor of how the different stages of our cultural evolution had inevitably undermined the top-down, zero sum approach of Big Men and their acolytes. Because there'd been limited anthropological research up to that time, they wouldn't have understood the way we'd been shaped by innovations and discoveries, nor would they have appreciated how each of these had added to the tensions of the various governance models.

> 'Human nature is… a hodgepodge of special genetic adaptations to an
> environment largely vanished, the world of the Ice Age hunter-gatherer.'
> EO Wilson, *On Human Nature*

Unlike the two well-meaning giants before him, Rousseau appears to have been a nasty piece of work. Diderot said he was 'false, vain as Satan, ungrateful, cruel, hypocritical and wicked'. Not exactly the kind of thing one likes to read on LinkedIn endorsements. Among his other shortcomings, Rousseau continued to live with the same poor seamstress for years, refusing to marry her and being endlessly vile and abusive. He insisted that she gave all their six children away to the foundling hospital before they could be given names, and even managed to fall out with the saintly David Hume, which really took some doing.

None of these things seemed to matter to devotees of Enlightenment thinking.

Jean-Jacques Rousseau. Not as nice as
he looks… and frequently wrong.

When Rousseau published his book, *du Contrat Social*, (thus grabbing the branding rights) it was seen by many as the intellectual blue touch paper for the moral uprising that led to the French Revolution.

What did Rousseau say in it? Well, if man was originally and naturally free, pure and simple, he argued, then it wasn't his fault that he'd become corrupted by society's rotten hierarchies, nor its various stratifications of authority. It was these that had made him envious, not his natural drives, and the result of living with the pressures of top-down edicts had led him to become greedy, unequal and competitive.

Since that was the case, Rousseau said, then surely the general *will* of the people should reverse it? But where to start? Well, because the root cause of so much of the conflict and confrontation one could see in society was the corrosive influence of private property, it was this that had to be controlled by the group as a whole.

> **'The first man who, having fenced in a piece of land, said 'this is mine' and found people naïve enough to believe him, that man was the true founder of civil society. From how many crimes, wars and murders, from how many horrors and misfortunes might anyone have saved mankind, by pulling up the stakes?'**
> **Jean-Jacques Rousseau, *Discourse of the Origin of Inequality***

The social contract, therefore, meant that while we obviously needed an authority to give us rules and control the process of human interaction, this had to be *legitimate*. It should be subject to laws and agreements, and periodically examined by people who should come together in a democratic way to discuss and decide whether it was fit for purpose. We didn't have to be against the principle of kings and aristocrats, Rousseau therefore concluded, but if these Big Men weren't judged by 'all citizens' to be legitimate then force was justified. And if they were really believed to be acting against the wishes of the masses - then off with their heads.

Off, indeed, the heads came. And revolutionary shocks like this meant that by the end of the 18th century, Enlightenment opposition to anything that wasn't *rational* - to things like myths, superstitions, the use of Latin, religious mysteries, secret societies and the like - was so complete that society's pendulum now swung decisively away from the presumption of authority. People like Newton, Hooke, Locke, Voltaire, Jefferson, Diderot, Rousseau and all their brilliant pals now knew so much, went the new thinking, that they could solve anything.

In other words, we needed more people like them and far less from the boss class and religious scaremongers, people spouting mumbo jumbo and promoting themselves as rulers. People whose instincts were to stick together while they kept the common man down were at the root of social malaise. Education, scientific discovery and rational deduction was what should now matter above all else.

The new mercantile middle-class loved it all. They, themselves, might be uneducated in the classical sense because the old kinds of knowledge and authority had been the province of the Church, medicine and the law. But power had now shifted decisively their way, and they were increasingly enjoying the opportunities that were coming with the reshaping of mankind's collective memes. Like new species after a mass extinction, trade now began to boom in the post-revolutionary period. The old hostilities were put to one side, and an age of more equitable wealth generation took off - less directed from on high, and more driven by the general growth of non-zero, prosperous interactions.

The anthropologist Alan Macfarlane has written about how 'internal predation… the predation of priests, lords, kings and even over-powerful merchant guilds… (had reduced) productive growth'. Now, with the old order having had their claws removed, the little man could move on. Macfarlane continued with his view that: '… after a period of anarchy and confusion, where productivity was low but flexibility was high', countries and their economies could now, '… settle down into higher productivity, but declining flexibility.'

If the vomiting of revolutionary bile was coming to an end, did the patient feel any better? Yes, indeed, seems to be the overall conclusion. In her book, *The Bourgeois Virtues*, the economist Deirdre McCloskey explains how the global upheavals were now being followed by boring, middle class traders who were bringing peace and prosperity to the system. As she puts it, the legacy of the revolutionary period was the introduction of: '… a new dignity and liberty for ordinary people (and they now)… applied to economic behaviour the seven old words of virtue - prudence, justice, courage, temperance, faith, hope and love.'

In this and its sister volume, *Bourgeois Dignity*, McCloskey sums up the transitions that were taking place between pre and post-revolutionary societies. They were, she concludes: 'The aristocratic virtues elevate an I. The Christian and peasant virtues elevate a Thou. The priestly virtues elevate an It. But the bourgeois virtues speak instead of We.'

'I do think one success of Northern Europe… was its willingness to accept innovation in business practices like Adam Smith and the whole Enlightenment. It essentially made the merchant class free instead of controlled by the king and the aristocracy.'
James Watson, *Avoid Boring People*

But what was going on? How were these 'virtues' coming through when the hand of the governing class was managing the economic process far less than it had done before? It was because, just as cooperation is needed in Nature for symbioses and synergies to overcome the entropic predictions of the 2nd Law of Thermodynamics, so the division of labour, and specialisation and exchange, were now increasingly working for the group benefit of our societies.

The key beliefs of Hobbes, Locke, Rousseau and so many others had been that laws, together with political and economic order, had not arisen naturally, but were human creations. This made them the product of our intellectual abilities, because they stemmed from our unique genius for examining the evidence and then taking decisions about the future.

But what these great philosophers and the later social contract eggheads such as Proudhon, de Tocqueville, John Stuart Mill and all the others were saying - let alone the mass of political philosophers that would come after them like Marx, Engels, Owen, those weird know-alls Sidney and Beatrice Webb and, yes, even Hitler, Stalin and Mao - in other words, everyone who knew better than the plebs about how to run the world, was that coming up with a solution to how society should operate was a process for the *intellect*.

If one thought hard enough about the issues, they all said (meaning themselves), then it was possible to dream up solutions to how mankind should live.

But from the middle of the 18th century onwards, society was showing that the most powerful directional force shaping it wasn't due to accepted beliefs, but instead, was coming up from below. It was no longer individual leaders who'd be deciding on the fate of ordinary men and women... but these people themselves would increasingly be saying how they wanted to live.

In other words the 'common man' was finally managing to slough off the ancient meme that their futures would be dictated to them by their 'superiors'. Trading, knowledge exchange, information, consumption and transport were what would bring about the changes, and these were all bottom-up vectors, the impact of which were becoming ever more evident in people's daily lives.

Now someone was about to emerge who would see what all this meant. He was going to show that the way to structure society wasn't to imagine what humans would have been like in a State of Nature, nor to tell us what would be best for people. Instead, his conviction was that what actually mattered in society could be arrived at by looking at how we humans *behaved*. Why was that? It was because if we did this it would show us what we really wanted in the real world.

What we should be trying to do, in short, was to work out what the currents of life meant, rather than trying to make sense of the waves.

Astonishingly, 250 years later, this simple idea still remains more important than any amount of social contract theory. Even today, many commentators are convinced that if human societies simply followed his rules, we'd all become wealthier and fairer, more moral and easier to govern.

Whaaaaat? Who was this?

Well, his name was Adam Smith.

Picture credits

Cover and end papers: Details from Pink Cava Lily by Bruce McLean. Copyright, the artist. Published by CCA Galleries, London and printed by Coriander Studios. Reproduced by kind permission of Bruce McLean and the CCA Galleries, September, 2022

Introduction: Alamy

Chapter 1:   Alamy, The March of Progress by Rudolph Zallinger 1965

Chapter 2:   ©Look and Learn/Bridgeman Images, iStock/Getty Images

Chapter 3:   www.CartoonStock.com, Mike Williams, in author's collection

Chapter 4:   Mike Williams, in author's collection, Alamy

Chapter 5:   Alamy

Chapter 6:   Alamy, C. Henshilwood and F d'Errico/ researchgate.net, Alamy

Chapter 7:   Author's collection

Chapter 8:   Bridgeman Images, Mike Williams, in author's collection

Chapter 9:   Alamy, Getty Images

Chapter 10:   Shutterstock, Alamy

Chapter 11:   Alamy, Bridgeman Images

Chapter 12:   www.CartoonStock.com, Alamy

Chapter 13:   Don Grant, author's collection, Source unknown,

Chapter 14:   Source unknown, www.CartoonStock.com

Chapter 15:   © British Library Board. All Rights Reserved/Bridgeman Images

Chapter 16:   Alamy, www.CartoonStock.com

Chapter 17:   Alamy